END TIME
Machine

END TIME
Machine

UNLOCKING THE MYSTERY BETWEEN
THE RAPTURE AND THE SECOND COMING

Kelli Nelson

Scripture quotations marked NIV are taken from THE HOLY BIBLE, NEW
INTERNATIONAL VERSION®, NIV® Copyright © 1973, 1978, 1984, 2011
by Biblica, Inc.® Used by permission. All rights reserved worldwide.

Scripture quotations marked AMP are taken from the
Amplified® Bible (AMP), Copyright © 2015 by The
Lockman Foundation. Used by permission.
www.Lockman.org

Scripture quotations marked ESV are taken from the ESV®
Bible (The Holy Bible, English Standard Version®), copyright
© 2001 by Crossway, a publishing ministry of Good News
Publishers. Used by permission. All rights reserved.

Scripture quotations marked KJV are taken from
the Holy Bible, King James Version.

First Edition
ISBN 978-1-956019-84-1(hardcover)
ISBN 978-1-956019-83-4 (paperback)
ISBN: 978-1-956019-85-8 (ebook)

Library of Congress Number: 2022946207

Maps and scrolls illustrated by Jennifer Levine.
Cover photo by Darvin Atkeson.

**Canoe Tree
Press**

4697 Main Street
Manchester Center, VT 05255

Canoe Tree Press is a division of DartFrog Books

"In your hearts regard Christ the Lord as holy, always being prepared to make a defense to anyone who asks you for a reason for the hope that is in you, yet do it with gentleness and respect."

—1 Peter 3:15-16

Contents

Introduction

The primary setting of this book is a courtroom in a fictitious small town. The townspeople are divided in their beliefs concerning the rapture and the second coming of Christ. Both sides agree, however, that the Bible is the Word of God. They both believe the Bible was written by God, through the Holy Spirit, through real people who lived long ago. They believe what is written in the Bible is true.

Both sides also agree upon a basic definition of the future event commonly referred to as the rapture: a moment in time when the followers of Jesus Christ will be transformed from mortal to immortal, the Lord himself will descend from heaven, the dead in Christ will rise first, and then we who are alive (who are left) will be caught up together with them in the clouds to meet the Lord in the air (1 Thessalonians 4:16-17).

The disagreement between the two sides is found in the timing of the rapture. Does the rapture happen before or after the final seven years? How will we know when the final seven years have begun? These are the central questions addressed in the trial.

Scripture in bold text is the author's emphasis.

~Kelli Nelson

Are you gearing up to disappear?

or

Are you gearing up for the world's greatest revival?

Prologue

Project Boomerang was finally ready for operational testing. DARPA's* time machine project began after World War II. It was financed by the United States Government and several defense contractors to pursue the theoretical implications of Einstein's general theory of relativity. The machine was hidden in an underground complex, underwater, next to DARPA's particle accelerator in Northern Minnesota. The Iron Range provided the electromagnetic energy source necessary to power the vessel. The water provided a sound barrier for departure and re-entry.

Project Boomerang is one of DARPA's longest standing and most secretive Special Access Programs, commonly known as Black Programs. All the engineers, scientists, military personnel, and support professionals were cleared for Top Secret/ Sensitive Compartmentalized Information (TS-SCI), which required them to have cover stories for their careers to conceal the unacknowledged program. Even their closest loved

---

* Defense Advanced Research Projects Agency

ones were kept from knowing their real objective: designing and building a time machine.

Lieutenant Colonel Ben Grant was assigned as the chief test pilot for Project Boomerang. Project directors began grooming Grant for this role fifteen years earlier after he gained a reputation as a tactical genius and brilliant engineer during his first operational assignment as a fighter pilot in the F-117 Nighthawk, a product of another long-term DARPA project.

After the F-117 officially retired in 2008, Captain Grant went to USAF Weapons School, one of the US Air Force's most arduous training programs. A distinguished graduate, he went on to write the first tactics manual for the F-22 Raptor. After several operational tours, Lieutenant Colonel Grant was handpicked to attend Air Force Test Pilot School (TPS) at Edwards Air Force Base in California, where he also earned a PhD in astrophysics from Stanford as part of a joint program. During his time at TPS, he flew many unacknowledged vehicles in development, culminating in his first official test assignment: Project Boomerang.

Chapter 1

The Time Machine

The time machine launched! Ben understood his unique position as pilot of the top-secret, highly classified, and largely unbelievable test mission. Their first destination? The great pyramids in ancient Egypt. One of history's biggest mysteries is how the pyramids of Giza were built. The historians, scientists, and linguists on board were thrilled with the prospect of discovering, even witnessing, the truth. Everyone anticipated an experience of a lifetime: traveling through time.

A moment after departure, an alert sounded on the vessel's master caution panel. Ben noticed the digital GPS coordinates fading in and out. The numbers were changing on their own. Not only was their destination in question, but the year was a mystery, too. He checked his other controls; nothing else indicated trouble.

Within minutes, the vehicle slowed down—as if it had chosen a distinct moment in time for its passengers. Ben did a quick recon and safely landed in a clearing. Taking precautions, the team sent out a scout. Once they received an "all clear," the travelers exited the vessel with wide eyes. They were gripped with excitement and relief, and they were in some disbelief. The atmosphere and surroundings were completely foreign, and while they still needed to investigate, the team members knew this: they weren't in Minnesota anymore! The voyage had been relatively quick and smooth, and no one was out of sorts physically as a result of traveling through time. Dr. Amy Stuart was onboard in case medical attention was needed.

The clearing was amidst trees and thick foliage. This was baffling because there were no pyramids in sight, and according to all of their calculations, they should have arrived when and where construction was in full swing. Furthermore, no people were in the immediate vicinity. Ben explained that the GPS glitched during transport, so he couldn't be sure of the exact time or place they had landed.

Eager for more information, the team sent up tiny surveillance drones. Video was transmitted back to the vessel. The images were shocking.

Ben exclaimed, "Look! Dinosaurs! It worked! We traveled back in time!"

Amy was astonished. "Unbelievable! This is incredible! Wow!"

Next, they saw something of considerable size approximately ten miles away. As the drones got closer, the image looked like some sort of wooden structure—perhaps a ship of some kind. However, it was not in water, so what could it be? According to the data coming from the drones, the structure was 450 feet long, 75 feet wide, and 45 feet high.[1] The image showed what looked to be one huge door on the side of the structure.

Ben looked at Amy and said, "Are you thinking what I'm thinking?"

"I don't know. What are you thinking?" she replied.

Ben whispered, "I bet that's Noah's Ark. Do you think we could have found Noah's Ark?"

"I don't know, but we should definitely check it out," Amy said with excitement.

Ben told everyone to get back on board. He pushed a few buttons on the control panel, and shortly, the ship was lifting off, fueled by zero-point anti-gravitational technologies. The mini drones were navigating the time machine, floating silently and cloaked from view to the desired destination. They flew right past a dinosaur's head and team members were taking pictures from the window. They set down in an area where no one would accidentally bump into an invisible time machine. Seeing all the various dinosaurs along the way from the air was an experience none of them would ever forget.

As the team disembarked, they were all in awe. A few of them were still wondering about the pyramids, but they were absolutely captivated by what they were seeing right before their eyes: a completed ark as described in the Bible. Ben and Amy convinced the team to abandon their search for the pyramids and to stay where they were for the next several days. The time machine was designed to accommodate fifteen people and six days' worth of food and supplies. The vessel was also equipped with sleeping quarters.

They spent six days observing, testing the atmosphere with special equipment, and gathering all kinds of soil samples and plants, along with pictures and video. They were even able to record footage inside Noah's Ark with tiny, undetectable drones.

Each day they witnessed animals entering the ark. Ben made it his goal to determine who Noah was and perhaps get video of him and his family entering the ark. He was able to disguise himself and discreetly capture the people on video as he walked among them. On their final day, they watched the gigantic door close.[2] They knew it was time to return to the present. Ben set the time machine to return to July 22, 2019, at 9:59 a.m., one minute before they had left on Monday. When they arrived home, it was 10:02 a.m., two minutes after they left. So, even though they experienced six days in the past, essentially no time had passed for those still in the present. The travelers came off the machine with excitement and could not wait to share their findings. The base team was waiting for them with anticipation. Even though the machine was only absent for two minutes, the uncertainty had made those minutes feel like hours.

So many questions will now need to be answered. Will they be able to keep this event a secret? Probably not. What happened to the clock panel? Can they fix it? Will it be reliable? Where will they attempt to go next? Who will get to go? How will it be decided? What will be the purpose of the next trip? Will they still try to see the pyramids being constructed? At some point, will private citizens be able to make reservations? How much will it cost for tourists to go back in time? Will another machine be built? Will science and history books be rewritten? Will people eventually come to terms that what is written in the Bible is true? All of these controversial issues will need to be addressed.

Chapter 2

The Town Trial

A my Stuart, MD, and her husband, Oliver Stuart, live in Cherry Creek, a small town in western Minnesota. In addition to her years of medical experience, Amy was recruited to be on the time machine mission because of her advanced research studies in quantum physics at Harvard. Oliver is the local district attorney and Ben's best friend since their college days at the University of Minnesota.

A few years ago, a community Bible study was started in which members of different churches came together to meet new people and build relationships. About a year ago, the leaders of the group took a survey and an overwhelming majority of the members said they wanted to study the prophecies in the Bible relating to the end times. They wanted to know more about the Antichrist, the seven trumpets, the seven seals, the mark of the beast, the prophesied one-world government, the Battle of Armageddon, and many other matters relating to the end times. The study became the place to be on Wednesday nights in Cherry Creek, and attendance soared.

People had various opinions about the timing of the rapture. Most leaned toward the pre-tribulation position, meaning that one day, all the Christians will instantly disappear, leaving the unbelievers left on earth for a terrible tribulation period of seven years. Some on the opposite end believed Christians will remain on earth throughout the final seven years, commonly referred to as the post-tribulation view. A few thought the rapture might happen sometime during the middle. Some believed "the end" will not happen in our lifetime. Several people just came to the group to socialize and listen to what everyone else had to say.

No matter the discussion topic of the week, the conversation almost always came back to the timing of the rapture. Over time, people went around and around repeating the same scriptures and the same arguments for their reasoning. Eventually, some participants quit attending.

Oliver came up with an unusual plan: hold court, allowing each side to present its case in a formal setting, without interruption by the opposing side. Word spread through the mom groups, the church softball league, the pastor's association, and the local hangouts. The idea caught on and the townspeople got excited. Although skeptical about the process, a judge was found to oversee the trial. A date would need to be set, and both sides would need time to prepare their case. Oliver volunteered to be the attorney representing the post-tribulation rapture. A small search committee was formed to find a qualified attorney who would volunteer to make a case for the pre-tribulation position.

Chapter 3

Six Days

Secret Underground Complex. Northern Minnesota.
Monday 10:02 a.m.

The time travelers were thankful to return safely and immediately began showing their pictures and video to the base team. All involved were sworn to absolute secrecy, at least for the time being. Technically, only two minutes had passed since they left, but the travelers missed their spouses and families. They spent the morning debriefing.

While eating lunch with the crew, Ben asked Amy, "What's new with you and Oliver in Cherry Creek?"

"Everyone in town is in a big debate about the timing of the rapture of the church. Oliver came up with the idea to hold court and have each side present their case in a formal setting. He volunteered to make the case for a post-tribulation rapture."

"When is the trial going to happen?"

"Oh, it already started. In fact, Holly should be wrapping up soon with her pre-trib arguments. The trial is being run a little bit out of the ordinary. One side presents, then the other. No interruptions by the opposing side when one side is 'up to bat' so to speak."

"Holly? Are you talking about Oliver's sister Holly? Doesn't she live in Texas?"

"Yeah, crazy right? Should be quite the trial. She and her husband and kids drove up for it. They usually visit in the summer so the boys can spend time with their grandparents. When Holly found out about the trial, she volunteered to make the case for a pre-tribulation rapture. There aren't too many trial lawyers that would take their vacation time to work. But both Holly and Oliver are convinced they are right, and the other is wrong. The townspeople remember Holly because she grew up there, so it was an easy choice. I wish I could have been there to see her make her case."

"Is Oliver going to be calling witnesses?"

"I have no idea. I've been focused on Project Boomerang, and I'm glad Oliver has been busy and focused on his case. He hasn't asked me any questions, and now it's going to be really hard to keep this a secret. Can you believe we just saw Noah and the animals entering the ark?"

"Well, I just had a great idea. What if we could go back in time and bring back the apostles Paul and John and a few others for Oliver to bring to the witness stand?"

"Oh, Ben! Do you think that's even possible? I think that might cause a lot of problems," she said anxiously. "We don't even know if the time machine is reliable."

"It sure would be fun if we could pull it off!" Ben said. "See if you can figure out when Oliver is up and see what else you can find out without letting on to what we are thinking. In the meantime, maybe I can get some GPS coordinates and a specific date to target."

"What about getting permission to use the time machine?"

"Yeah, I don't think that's going to fly. 'Small Town Uses Time Machine to Gather Witnesses for Rapture Case.' Sounds hilarious. They would just suggest using the machine to go to the future to find out when the rapture happens."

"I never thought about that. Can this machine go into the future?"

"No. The panel doesn't accept dates when you try to program it for the future. In order to get back to the present, I couldn't even set the time for 10:00 a.m., the same time we left. I had to set it for 9:59 a.m. in order for it to register."

"Interesting," Amy said. "I wonder if there are other glitches. If we do manage to bring, let's say, the apostle Paul to the present, is it possible to return him to his time without him remembering what happened while he was here?"

"If we return him to one minute before he left, it should work. I don't think he would remember his time here."

"What about security? How are we going to get access to the machine, and who else can we get to help us with the trip?"

"Well, we have some time to convince the others and see if we can come up with a game plan. Are you in?"

Amy hesitated for a moment, then agreed. "Sure, if you can convince the others."

After lunch, the base team resupplied the time machine and made plans for the team to depart again the next morning. The travelers had the afternoon to relax, call loved ones, and prepare for the next day. None of them lived close to the secret base location, and their loved ones were not expecting them home for a few days. Ben spent some time with the base engineers to see what might have caused the GPS malfunction.

The next morning at 9:00 a.m., they were off. The GPS coordinates were set to modern-day Iraq, five million years ago. Nobody really knew where the Garden of Eden was, but now that Noah's Ark was a verified fact, the scientists and historians wanted to push the envelope to see how far back the vessel would go and what they would discover.

No alarms went off during transport. When the machine slowed down, three minutes had elapsed since they left, according to Ben's wrist band. He couldn't see anything outside because it was dark, but he was able to land—on water! They suddenly realized that they couldn't send the scout. The numbers on the panel were spinning out of control, and once again, the team had no idea what year it was or where they were. They figured that they had arrived at night and would wait until morning to see where they were.

Amy had a pretty good idea of what was going on and what year it was. She didn't believe the vessel could go back before God created time. "How could we go back five million years if God created time starting at creation?" she thought. She could feel the Spirit of God hovering over the face of the waters.[1]

Amy had read Genesis chapters one and two so many times; she whispered to herself, "In the beginning, God created the heavens and the earth. The earth was without form and void, and darkness was over the face of the deep." A chill went up her spine. She had goosebumps all over and could not wait to see what would unfold before their eyes over the next few days.

A few hours went by, and suddenly, there was light. All they could see was water and light. Nothing else. The light was not coming from the sun. They sent up drones. No data came back, and the only images were of light and water. The atmosphere felt completely different from home, and they couldn't see the sky. It was very strange. So they sat around inside the time machine for a whole day. They discussed all kinds of theories and wondered if they should hit the emergency "back" button and go home. Amy and Ben had a fairly good idea of what was coming and convinced the others to stick it out a few more days to see what would happen.

On the second day, they witnessed the creation of the sky. It was an extraordinary experience, but they were restless at the same time. Two days had gone by. They wanted to get out and explore, like when they saw Noah's Ark, but they still couldn't leave the time machine. They sent up drones again. Nothing. No data came back. Only sky and water.

"If my calculations are correct," Amy spoke up, "we will see dry land tomorrow."

Mark, one of the paleontologists on board, said, "What do you mean 'your calculations'?"

Amy answered, "Well, it appears to me we are witnessing the creation of the world as described in the book of Genesis. When we got here, it was dark. In the Bible, God said, 'Let there be light, and there was light.'[2] We saw light, not the sun, created. Believe it or not, it looks to me like we are going to watch God create the sun on our fourth day.[3] On the second day, we saw the sky, or as the Bible calls it, 'an expanse' or a 'firmament,' created. God called the expanse Heaven.[4] Tomorrow will be the third day. On the third day, according to the Bible, God said, 'Let the waters under the heavens be gathered together into one place, and let the dry land appear. He called the dry land Earth, and the waters that were gathered together He called Seas.'[5] I can't wait to see it!"

Mark looked at Ben and said, "What about you? Do you agree with her? Do you think we will see land tomorrow?"

Ben said with a big smile, "Yep. I sure do!"

While she had a captive audience, Amy got out her Bible and read to them the creation account in Genesis. Team members went back and forth and debated different theories all day, and Amy did her best to explain from her perspective what they just witnessed regarding the firmament, or as God called the expanse, Heaven. They eventually went to sleep that night in anticipation of the next day.

Amy knew that many schools and universities teach evolution as a fact—that the earth is millions and even billions of years old. However, Amy disagreed with the theory of evolution. As a medical doctor, a scientist, and a Christian, Amy believed the scientific evidence confirms the biblical account of creation. She shared with everyone on board about her visit to the Creation Museum and Ark Encounter in Kentucky.

On day three, they watched as God created land before their eyes, just as Amy and Ben knew He would. The time machine was on dry land now, so they could get out, explore, go on a walk, and take pictures and video. On the same day, they saw the earth sprout vegetation. Plants yielded seed, and fruit trees bore fruit. [6] Trees sprang up from the earth, fully grown. An unbelievable event! It didn't happen over millions and millions of years. They walked all over in amazement, touching the trees that were not there the day before and picking fruit to eat. They sent up drones and captured plenty of images and data to analyze.

As Amy expected, the brilliant sun appeared in the sky on the fourth day.[7] That night, they witnessed the moon and stars for the first time since they had arrived. They had yet to see any animals or birds. Many on the team were bewildered. Their whole worldview was being challenged right before their eyes. For those who wanted to listen, Amy gave her opinions and brought up thought-provoking questions.

"Think about this," she said. "Let's say for a moment that God created the world in six days like we are watching it happen and like it's written in the Bible. Let's also say, for argument's sake, that the Bible is true and that God wrote it. Would it be logical then, if God detailed for us the beginning of the earth, that He would also include in the Bible specific details and events that will occur at the end of the earth as we know it?" She went on and shared with them about her husband's court case and the opposing theories regarding the final seven years, but that both sides agreed they were living near the end of time. This was a new idea for many of them; however, it got them thinking, and some of them agreed that it made sense.

On the fifth day, they woke up to a sky full of birds. They were not near any water, so they couldn't see any fish or great sea creatures.[8] The creation account described in the Bible was unfolding right before their eyes. Some of the people on the team were still in denial and having a difficult time. They still wanted to believe that the earth was millions and billions of years old. Others had changed their minds completely. They were eager to get to day six, to see if what was written in the Bible would actually happen.

On the sixth day, God created all of the land animals.[9] They could see animals everywhere they looked. They had not seen any animals the day before or any on the days before that. That did it! Everyone in the group was now convinced that God created the world and everything in it, in six twenty-four-hour days. There was no more debate. According to Amy's Bible, God also created man on this day: "male and female He created them."[10] Even though they did not see Adam or Eve, they knew they were there somewhere on the earth.

Their wrist bands started beeping. This meant they had one hour to get back on board. The time machine would leave with or without them. Their wrist bands were a fail-safe mechanism to let them know when their time was up and they had to return to the present. Even though a week had gone by for the travelers, when they got home, it was still Tuesday morning, 9:02 a.m.—only two minutes after they had left.

During the last few days of the trip, as team members could no longer deny that the Bible was true, Ben and Amy had opportunities to talk with them individually regarding the court case in progress and ask if they wanted to be involved in a covert operation of their own, without the government's knowledge. Ben's enthusiasm was contagious, and they didn't want to miss out.

The team had the rest of the day to debrief, relax, and make the necessary arrangements for later that night. No more voyages were scheduled. The base team was not yet ready to let the media and the entire world in on their time machine endeavors, but they did want to capture and preserve the immediate excitement of the time travelers. They spent part of the day recording interviews with Ben, Amy, and the others on the team for broadcast at a later time. Many decisions had to be made over the next week.

Chapter 4

Operation Transport

It was late on Tuesday, and the base was quiet. Ben and the others knew they would get into trouble if they were caught, but they thought the risk was worth it. They had seen too much and were ready for a challenge. Their secret mission was to bring the apostle Paul to the present in order to help Oliver with his court case.

Ben had spoken to a few Bible experts and done some research for best guess GPS coordinates. He set the clock for AD 66. After punching in the numbers, they were off. A few minutes later, they arrived in Rome. Ben arranged for a linguist who spoke several languages, including ancient Greek, Hebrew, and Aramaic, to accompany them on this trip so that they could attempt to communicate with the local people while searching for Paul. They didn't know what he looked like, so they were not sure how they would identify him, other than asking, "Do you know where we can find Paul, the healer?"

Once they found him, they were overcome with admiration and excitement. They were able to somewhat convince him that they were from the future by taking a picture and showing him the image. Paul was most curious and agreed to follow them to see what this was all about. They led him to where they had hidden the time machine and then turned off the cloaking device. He had never seen anything like it and was shocked, curious, and suspicious all at the same time. "Where did this come from?" he thought. He followed them onto the vessel because he wanted to see inside. They did their best to explain to him that they wanted him to travel with them into the future. He was not really listening because he was focused on what he was seeing. The lights, the images on screens, the unfamiliar writing—everything was foreign to him.

While Paul was distracted by everything, the crew closed the doors and got ready for departure. Paul noticed that they were sitting in fancy chairs and getting buckled in. He followed their example with assistance from one of the team members.

On the return trip, Ben set the GPS coordinates to Amy and Oliver's property in Cherry Creek. It was an ideal spot because they lived on a farm with no neighbors for at least a mile in any direction. They arrived safe and undetected in the dark of night. The team dropped Amy and Paul off, got back in the machine, and left immediately to go back to AD 99 to search for the apostle John. They found him, advanced in years, just outside Ephesus in his hilltop home. Once they convinced the great apostle to go with them, they were off. And within minutes, they arrived back at the Stuart property.

Amy and Oliver gave Paul and John their own ear translation devices and demonstrated how to put them in. The new Convers8 translation devices were very popular among tourists and business travelers. They were also becoming more popular among the public. The device allowed for people who spoke different languages to communicate with each other. Before inviting Paul and John into their home, Amy and Oliver took them into the barn to give some explanation and answer some of their questions.

"We have brought you from your time to ours, approximately two thousand years into the future. It's an honor for us to bring you here and meet you in person, to see you and talk to you. Yes, we have temporarily interrupted your lives, but we assure you, when you go back to your time, you will go back to the same time and place you left."

Meanwhile, Ben reset the clock and coordinates to search for Daniel, a crucial witness for Oliver's case. Once they found Daniel and brought him to the Stuart property, Ben made one more trip. This time he went looking for Matthew. He left a few of his team with Amy and Oliver to help bring the guests up to speed.

The barn was full of hay, a couple of horses, one cow, and some chickens. All of this was somewhat familiar to their guests. Once they entered the house, a lot more explaining would be necessary. It was summertime, late July, and the night was comfortable for sleeping outside. Oliver had set up some temporary beds for them on the screen porch with blankets and pillows. After Matthew arrived, one of the first things they explained to all of them was the bathroom, the toilet, toilet paper, sinks, faucets, and light switches. They were fascinated with these conveniences.

Since John was an old man in his late nineties, Matthew didn't recognize him. John, however, recognized Matthew. After Amy explained and confirmed they were friends, they were in disbelief but wanted to know how this was possible, and more importantly, why they were there.

After more introductions, Paul realized who Matthew and John were, and they him. Daniel didn't know who anyone was, but everyone knew Daniel. Matthew, John, and Paul were thrilled to meet the prophet Daniel from the Scriptures. Daniel was bewildered that everybody knew several of his life stories. When he considered that maybe God had revealed these stories, it was more plausible to him. He gave glory to God for His sovereign works! The men spent most of the night talking on the screen porch. Oliver stayed up late with them too, explaining the court case and what to expect the next day.

Now that the great men of God had been transported to the Stuart farm, Ben set the time machine to return to the home base complex. He scheduled their arrival for 9:59 p.m., one minute before they had departed. As Ben hoped, they showed up only two minutes after they had left. They successfully bypassed security once again with help from a few of the people Ben had recruited from the first two trips. They were all in on this mission. While several of the team had time traveled with Ben, a few stayed behind to distract the 24/7 security. It was not hard to cover for a few minutes, especially since most of the guards did not know they were guarding a time machine. They thought it was a top-secret military weapon.

Ben and the ones who stayed behind left the complex undetected and headed directly to Cherry Creek. They were excited to get to know their guests and to observe the court hearing the next morning.

Chapter 5

Our Guests

Stuart Home. Cherry Creek, Minnesota.
Wednesday morning.

The honored guests watched everything that morning with eyes wide open. Oliver taught them how to use the shower. They loved the invention. Oliver also had some professional clothes and shoes in various sizes available for them. They all tried on the fancy apparel but decided to wear their own.

In the kitchen, Amy and a few of her time-traveling friends made breakfast for everyone. The day before, Oliver had picked up an assortment of fruits and vegetables to make sure they had plenty of familiar food to eat. Oliver poured cereal and milk into a bowl. He was in a hurry and ate fast so he could get to court. He grabbed a banana on the way out and said, "See you guys later."

The new arrivals had never seen a refrigerator, and they were not sure what Oliver had eaten from the box. The men were intrigued with the gas stove and watched intently as Amy cooked eggs. Next, they watched her take bacon out of the freezer and pop it into the microwave. That was another mystery. They didn't understand how the meat could be freezing cold and a minute later be hot and ready to eat. She knew the guests probably would not eat bacon, but the rest of the crew would. Cinnamon rolls were baking in the oven, with the oven light on so they could watch the rolls rise. So fascinating!

Daniel kept opening and shutting the refrigerator door, feeling the cold temperature and noticing the light inside. He was curious about the difference in temperature between the freezer and the refrigerator. John liked the kitchen sink. He kept turning the water on and off and changing the temperature from cold to hot, back and forth. Matthew was interested in both the toaster and the coffee maker, so Ben taught him how to make toast and coffee.

After breakfast, they watched as Amy and the others placed their dirty dishes in the dishwasher, shut the door, and pushed a button. They were amazed when Amy told them the dishes would be clean in an hour.

The men had never seen photos, and Matthew wanted to know more about them. Amy and Oliver had family photos displayed on the walls and all kinds of pictures on the refrigerator. Paul was trying to figure out how the magnets held up the pictures. John kept looking through all the books on the bookshelves. He couldn't read the print, but he recognized them as modern-day scrolls.

At 10:30 a.m., Ben got a text from Oliver telling him it was time to bring Paul to court. He was Oliver's first witness. Ben and Paul got in the car, leaving the others in the house. Since Paul had never seen a car, he wasn't quite sure what was going to happen next. Ben helped him get buckled in with the seat belt while explaining that the car would start moving and that they would go gradually faster. Ben also handed Paul a pair of sunglasses to wear. Paul put them on and said, "Fabulous! Wonderful concept. Can I take these home with me?" Ben took a selfie with Paul in the car wearing their sunglasses together.

As they drove down the road, Paul was a little uneasy at first but confident that Ben knew what he was doing. Ben threw in a CD playing George Frederic Handel's Messiah—the Hallelujah Chorus. "Wow," Paul said. "That sounds incredible!" After they arrived at the courthouse, Paul said to Ben, "What a fantastic experience! Do you think you can teach me how to drive this thing? It doesn't look too difficult. Actually, I think I can probably just figure it out by myself."

Meanwhile, back at the homestead, the other guests continued to investigate the house and ask more questions. They were so curious. Daniel started looking through the closets and drawers. He found the vacuum cleaner, and so another demonstration was in order. John was in one of the bedrooms and decided to lay down on the bed. How comfortable it was! He also found Amy's blow dryer. One of the gals plugged it in and demonstrated, pretending to dry her hair. He inquired about the toothbrushes and since they had extra ones in the house, they all brushed their teeth.

Matthew inquired about the big black TV screen on the wall and the other smaller computer monitors, but Amy decided to ignore those. Instead, she turned on the stereo and played some classical music. The guests were pleased and had big smiles on their faces.

The piano was a big attraction and little things were too, like clocks, pencils, pens, scissors, and all the different kinds of shoes and boots. The time-traveling crew members had a great time demonstrating how things worked, like the treadmill and the stationary bike. Matthew and John got on the odd contraptions and gave them a whirl. Neither of them could figure out why one would need such devices.

Chapter 6

That Day Will Not Come, Unless...

The windows were all open in the little courtroom in Cherry Creek, Minnesota. Next to the bench where the judge was sitting, an American flag stood tall. Behind the bench, written on the wall, were the words "In God We Trust." Holly Norton, the attorney arguing for a pre-tribulation rapture, had just finished presenting her case.

Her key arguments centered on proving that the rapture and the second coming of Jesus Christ to the earth are two different events, separated by a seven-year period. She also emphasized that no one knows the day or the hour and that God would not make His children suffer His wrath during the tribulation. Holly brought in several biblical scholars and theologians who testified about how the conditions in our world right now are as the Bible describes the last days. She knew she had successfully convinced the jury and the townspeople in the room that Jesus Christ will rapture His church at any moment—triggering the terrible tribulation period as well as the seven-year countdown to the Battle of Armageddon.

The opposing attorney, Oliver Stuart, was excited to make his case for a post-tribulation rapture. Having just heard what appeared to be a flawless pre-trib exposition, the people in the courtroom were wondering what Oliver could possibly say that would change anybody's mind.

He began, "Ladies and gentlemen of the jury, I'm going to present evidence that will overwhelmingly convince you, beyond a shadow of a doubt, that there are specific events which must take place before the rapture of the church. These events will be described in detail so that you will be able to recognize them when you see them. I will also present compelling evidence for the precise timing of the rapture of the church.

"Your Honor," he said. "I would like to call my first witness to the stand, the apostle Paul."

Holly stood up and said, "Objection! Your Honor, this is hogwash."

Judge Kane, who was presiding over the case, reminded Holly that both sides had agreed to make no objections during each other's presentations, so even though he agreed with her, he would allow Oliver to continue.

"Mr. Stuart, you may continue, but please don't waste the court's time," said the judge.

"Yes, of course. Your Honor, with your permission, I think this would be a good time to pass out the new Convers8 translation devices to everyone in court."

"The what?" replied Judge Kane.

"Allow me to explain, Your Honor."

"Very well, we will see how far this goes. Bailiff, please pass out the translation devices to everyone."

Oliver continued, "Your Honor, I now call the apostle Paul to the stand, and I encourage everyone to put in their translation devices, or TDs, at this time. Paul's ancient Greek will be translated into English so that we can understand him, and he will understand me because my English is being translated into Greek."

The jurors looked at the judge and each other, confused. The townspeople began murmuring amongst themselves. Judge Kane sighed and said, "Very well, if you want to keep up this silly act, counselor, you may continue. It's your case."

"Thank you, Your Honor" Oliver said. "Welcome, Paul. It is a great honor to have you with us today. Sir, for the record, please state your name."

"Paul, formerly Saul."

"Where are you from, Paul?"

"I was born in Tarsus, in Cilicia, and I am a citizen of Rome."

As Paul began, everyone could hear him speaking in what sounded like a foreign language. They could also hear the words being translated into English through their TDs. The judge, jury, and townspeople were impressed with the technology but were surprised that Oliver would hire an actor to impersonate the great apostle. Paul's language sounded authentic, even though no one in the courtroom had ever heard ancient Greek. "Oliver went over the top this time," they thought, "hiring someone who speaks Greek and pretends to be the apostle Paul to serve as a visual aid."

"Got to hand it to him," one of the jurors said, "he sure has our attention."

"Yeah," someone else agreed, "he really outdid himself this time. I wonder where he found those old clothes. They even smell authentic."

"What is your occupation, Paul?" Oliver asked.

"By trade, I am a tentmaker. However, I became a missionary called by Christ Jesus to preach the good news."

The jurors and townspeople snickered a bit. "He is playing his part well!" someone whispered.

"Did you have a religious upbringing, Paul?"

"Yes."

"Please describe for us your religious background."

"I was born and raised in a Jewish home. My father was a Pharisee, as was I. As an adult, I was a persecutor of the people who followed the man named Jesus. Eventually, however, I became a follower and servant of the Lord Jesus Christ."

"What circumstances led you to decide to follow Jesus Christ?"

"Well, one day, I was traveling to the city of Damascus. I was prepared to take captive anyone belonging to the Way, or the followers of Jesus. Suddenly, a light from heaven flashed around me. I heard a voice saying 'Saul, Saul, why are you persecuting me?' The voice said, 'I am Jesus, whom you are persecuting.'

Although my eyes were open, I could not see. After three days, God sent a man named Ananias, who laid his hands on me, and my sight was restored. I was filled with the Holy Spirit and baptized. My whole life changed, even my name."[1]

Everyone in the room except the judge and Holly started clapping. They thought this man was an actor and was doing a very good job playing the part of Paul.

Oliver continued, "So, Paul, according to your letters, in addition to making tents, you then became a teacher and traveled as you taught. In fact, you wrote several widely circulated letters to the saints in Rome, to the church in Corinth, to the churches of Galatia, to the saints in Ephesus, to the saints at Philippi, to the saints at Colossae, to the church of the Thessalonians, and more. Is that correct?"

"Yes, that is correct."

"Paul, most of the people in our town believe we are getting close to the end of the age and the rapture of the church. We are in disagreement as to when the rapture is going to happen, and we don't want to go through the tribulation period. Some of us believe we will be raptured soon—any day now—which will then begin the final seven years. Others believe we will be raptured at the end of the seven years. We have read your letters over and over, and we have invited you here today, to the year 2019, so that you can tell us in your own words when the rapture of the church will happen." Oliver walked closer to the stand. "In your expert opinion, Paul, when do you say the rapture will happen?"

"Sure. Absolutely. Remind me again, Mr. Stuart, what exactly are you referring to when you use the word rapture?"

"Well, Paul, according to your own words that you wrote to the Thessalonian church, you describe what we call the rapture as, and I'm quoting you, 'Now concerning the coming of our Lord Jesus Christ and our being gathered together to him.' You also refer to it as 'the day of the Lord.'"[2]

"Very well, Mr. Stuart, as you know according to my letter 'that day will not come, unless the rebellion comes first, and the man of lawlessness is revealed, the son of destruction, who opposes and exalts himself against every so-called god or object of worship, so that he takes his seat in the temple of God, proclaiming himself to be God.'"[3]

"Thank you, Paul. Ladies and gentlemen of the jury, you have just heard it directly from the apostle Paul himself, the day will not come unless two specific things happen. First, the rebellion must occur, and second, the rapture will not happen until the man of lawlessness is revealed. Paul, are you specifically telling us the rapture cannot happen at any time before the man of lawlessness is revealed?"

"Yes, that is correct."

"Sir, the third thing you mentioned is that the man of lawlessness will be revealed when he sits in the temple of God and proclaims himself to be God. What temple are you talking about? Where is this temple?"

"Well, in Jerusalem, of course."

"Paul, currently there is no Jewish temple on the Temple

Mount in Jerusalem. There is an Islamic shrine called the Dome of the Rock and the Al-Aqsa Mosque, but no Jewish temple."

"I'm confused," Paul replied. "What happened to the temple?"

"I'm sorry to have to tell you this Paul, but the Romans destroyed the Jewish temple. The good news is that according to your writings, the temple will be rebuilt. According to what you just said, the man of lawlessness, and we refer to him as the Antichrist, will be revealed when he sits in the temple of God, so therefore, we know the temple will be rebuilt.

"So, to repeat what you said Paul, and this is important, you said the rapture, or the coming of our Lord Jesus Christ and our being gathered together to him, will not happen until the man of lawlessness sits in the temple of God, in Jerusalem, and proclaims himself to be God. Is that correct?"

"Yes. That is correct."

"Thank you, Paul. To summarize, ladies and gentlemen of the jury, we have now identified at least four things that must happen before the rapture of the church. I have them listed on the screen for you." Oliver gestured to a large flat screen where a PowerPoint was displayed. On it, the following points were listed:

1. *Rebellion occurs.*
2. *Antichrist is revealed to the world.*
3. *Temple must be rebuilt.*
4. *Antichrist will sit in the temple and proclaim himself God.*

Oliver read them aloud for the courtroom, then continued his argument. "Your Honor, for the purpose of this unusual case, and for the record, all exhibits have been marked and shown in advance to the opposing counsel in an exhibit binder. There have been no objections by opposing counsel to the exhibits being entered into evidence. All exhibits have met the necessary evidentiary requirements to be admitted. Also, I have an iPad here; I will type in the reference on the iPad, and the Scripture will come up in Greek for Paul to read aloud in his own language. With your permission, at this time, I would like to submit a portion of what Paul wrote to the church in Thessalonica for the jurors to read: Exhibit 1."

"Very well, counselor, you may proceed."

"Thank you, Your Honor. Ladies and gentlemen of the jury, the bailiff will now pass out copies of the exhibit binder to serve as a reference during the trial. At this time, I will ask Paul to read his own writing, Exhibit 1." Oliver handed the iPad to Paul and said, "Paul, will you please confirm this is, in fact, a portion of your own writing?"

After examining the illuminated screen with curiosity, Paul answered, "Yes, this is what I wrote to the church in Thessalonica. My, how tablets have changed over the centuries!"

"Thank you, Paul. Please read aloud Exhibit 1."

"Very well." Paul began reading in Greek. The exhibit was magnified onto a large flat screen in English so that everyone in the room could follow along. The jurors had their exhibit binders, and the Convers8 devices were translating everything Paul said into English.

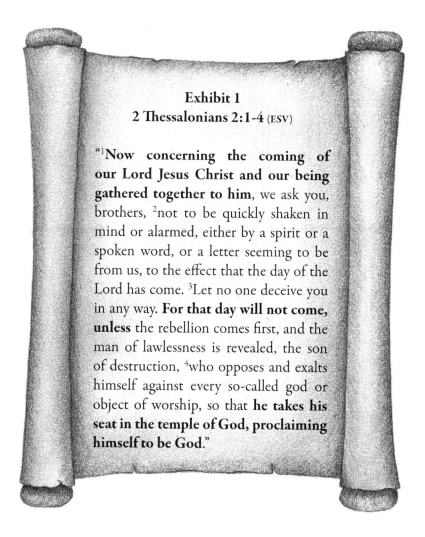

Exhibit 1
2 Thessalonians 2:1-4 (ESV)

"**¹Now concerning the coming of our Lord Jesus Christ and our being gathered together to him,** we ask you, brothers, ²not to be quickly shaken in mind or alarmed, either by a spirit or a spoken word, or a letter seeming to be from us, to the effect that the day of the Lord has come. ³Let no one deceive you in any way. **For that day will not come, unless** the rebellion comes first, and the man of lawlessness is revealed, the son of destruction, ⁴who opposes and exalts himself against every so-called god or object of worship, so that **he takes his seat in the temple of God, proclaiming himself to be God.**"

"Ladies and gentlemen," Oliver continued, "as we have heard from the apostle Paul himself, the rapture can't possibly happen today, tomorrow, or next month because we must wait until the Jewish temple is built and the Antichrist is revealed. He will take his seat in the temple and proclaim himself to be God."

At this point, the judge raised his gavel and announced, "We will take a break and reconvene at 1:30 p.m."

Chapter 7

The Dead in Christ Will Rise First

During the break, all the townspeople at the trial were talking about Paul, who they all assumed was an actor. They wanted to get their picture taken with him. Paul was enjoying the attention and noticed people carrying around small metal objects that reflected their images. They asked him to be in their "selfies," just like Ben had in the car. Once again, he saw his own image on the cell phone and wanted more information about the device. When he inquired about the phone, the people laughed and said to Oliver, "You went all out with this guy."

Many families brought picnic lunches to the trial. Amy and the crew arrived with John, Matthew, and Daniel. They brought food and blankets to sit on the grass. Paul and the two linguists joined the group. As the crew sat down to eat, Oliver explained that many people in the courtroom thought Paul was an actor.

Ben said to him, "You've got this, Ollie. Just make your case and take it one step at a time. We've got your back." The jurors all sat together inside, and lunch was brought to them. Holly kept her eyes on the one claiming to be Paul, and she noticed that he was eating lunch with three other people dressed in costumes similar to his. She wondered what Oliver was going to do next. After lunch, everyone returned into the courthouse.

The bailiff announced, "All rise. Court is now in session, the Honorable Judge Kane presiding."

Oliver began, "Your Honor, I would like to continue questioning the apostle Paul of Tarsus, citizen of Rome."

"Proceed."

"Thank you, Your Honor." Oliver turned his attention to the stand. "Paul, will you please read aloud for the court Exhibit 2, from the first letter you wrote to the church in Thessalonica?"

"Certainly. This is incredible how these letters have been preserved all this time into the future, and this device you call an iPad is extraordinary." Paul began reading in Greek. Everyone else was reading and listening in English.

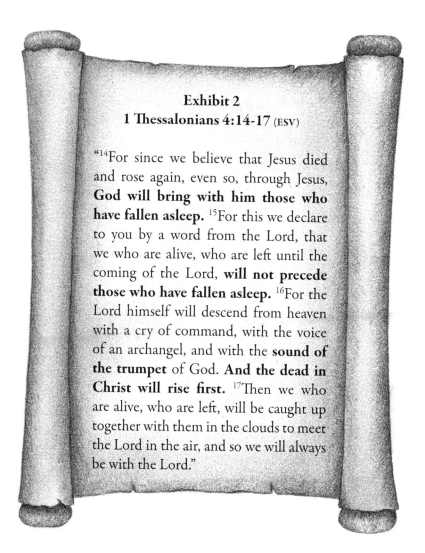

Exhibit 2
1 Thessalonians 4:14-17 (ESV)

"14For since we believe that Jesus died and rose again, even so, through Jesus, **God will bring with him those who have fallen asleep.** 15For this we declare to you by a word from the Lord, that we who are alive, who are left until the coming of the Lord, **will not precede those who have fallen asleep.** 16For the Lord himself will descend from heaven with a cry of command, with the voice of an archangel, and with the **sound of the trumpet** of God. **And the dead in Christ will rise first.** 17Then we who are alive, who are left, will be caught up together with them in the clouds to meet the Lord in the air, and so we will always be with the Lord."

"Paul, in this passage, when you say 'the dead in Christ will rise first,' who are you referring to? Who are the dead in Christ?"

"The dead in Christ are people who have already died, or 'fallen asleep,' people who, when they were alive, lived their lives pleasing God, as the Spirit of God dwelled in them. Anyone who did not have the Spirit of Christ living in them did not belong to God.[1] There would have been evidence in the way they lived their life whether they belonged to Christ or not."

Oliver continued, "Paul, you describe an event in this passage that both the pre-tribulation and post-tribulation camps agree is a description of what we refer to as the rapture of the church. As you stated, when Jesus Christ comes back to earth, He will bring with Him the Christians who have already died (the dead in Christ). This will happen at the sound of a trumpet, and the believers who are alive at the time together with the Christians who have already died will be caught up in the clouds to meet the Lord in the air. Is this correct?"

"Yes, except the dead in Christ will rise first, and then those who are still alive will be caught up together with them in the clouds to meet the Lord in the air."

"Thank you, Paul. Your Honor, I would like to present at this time Exhibit 3 to the jury: a portion of Paul's first letter to the church in Corinth."

"Very well, proceed."

"Thank you, Your Honor. Ladies and gentlemen of the jury, please refer to Exhibit 3 in your exhibit binder. Paul, will you please read aloud for the court Exhibit 3, from the first letter you wrote to the church in Corinth?"

"Certainly," Paul said before he began to read the excerpt aloud.

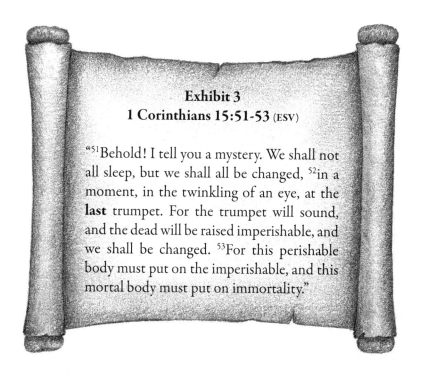

Exhibit 3
1 Corinthians 15:51-53 (ESV)

"[51]Behold! I tell you a mystery. We shall not all sleep, but we shall all be changed, [52]in a moment, in the twinkling of an eye, at the **last** trumpet. For the trumpet will sound, and the dead will be raised imperishable, and we shall be changed. [53]For this perishable body must put on the imperishable, and this mortal body must put on immortality."

"Thank you, Paul. I want to point out to everyone that both the pre-tribulation camp and the post-tribulation camp agree this passage of scripture is another description of the event we refer to as the rapture of the church." Looking back at Paul, Oliver said, "I'm curious about the trumpet part, Paul. In 1 Thessalonians 4:16, you describe the event happening, quote, 'For the Lord himself will descend from heaven with a cry and command, with the voice of an archangel, and with the sound of the trumpet of God.' You were more specific in your letter addressed to the Corinthian church and wrote that this event will happen at the *last* trumpet. Is that correct?"

"Yes, that is correct."

"Thank you, Paul. To summarize then, the 'dead in Christ' will rise first at the sound of the *last* trumpet, then those who are still here are 'changed' from mortal to immortal. Is that correct?"

"Yes, that is correct."

"Paul, another popular belief in our town is that people who are followers of Jesus, those who have repented of their sin and surrendered their lives to Christ, will suddenly just disappear at the time of the rapture. However, in your letter to the church in Corinth, you don't say we will disappear. You say, 'we shall be changed.' Is that correct?"

"Yes. That is correct; from mortal to immortal."

"Thank you, sir." Oliver turned to the judge. "Your Honor, I would like to recall this witness at a later time."

"Very well, Paul, you may step down. Please continue, Mr. Stuart."

Chapter 8

The Last Trumpet

The entire courtroom was curious to see what Oliver would do next. They observed three more people in costumes sitting near him in the front row. Holly was a little upset by Oliver's tactics, but she admitted to herself that the apparent authenticity of these actors made for a great visual aide and helped bring the Bible to life. It was almost like watching a play, and the actors had rehearsed and memorized their lines very well.

"Your Honor," Oliver said, "I would like to call my second witness to the stand, the apostle John, disciple of Jesus Christ." A murmur went through the room as John approached the stand. "John, welcome to the United States of America in the year 2019, and thank you for being here today. The people in our town believe we are living near the end of the age. We are in a debate over whether the rapture will happen at the beginning of the final seven years or at the end of the seven years."

Holding a Bible, the bailiff walked to the witness stand to perform the swearing-in. Judge Kane said, "John, please raise your right hand and place your left hand on the Holy Scriptures."

John replied, "These are the Holy Scriptures?"

"Yes."

"This object contains the entire Word of God?"

"Yes," Judge Kane replied. "All the writings of the Law and Prophets, together with the Gospels and the apostles' writings, have all been compiled together in one book we call the Holy Bible."

"Glory to God! How many copies have been transcribed?"

Judge Kane redirected to Oliver. "Counselor, will you please continue answering your witness's questions?"

"Yes, of course, Your Honor. My apologies. Well, let's see, John. Give me a second here and I will check my phone. It says here that in addition to five billion in printed form, there have been more than three hundred million downloads of the Holy Bible in digital form, in all countries of the world."[1]

John was excited. "Glory to God, the Most High! And are you telling me that my writings are included in this Holy Bible and people can carry them around with them everywhere they go?"

"Yes. The words have been translated into more than 700 languages, and by the year 1560 the Bible had been subdivided into chapters and verses, making it easier to pinpoint a specific passage when discussing it with others."[2,3]

"This is fascinating! Perhaps the people in your town are correct that you are getting close to the end of the age. If you are familiar with the prophet Daniel's writings, he wrote that in the time of the end, knowledge shall increase. From what you have described, knowledge has increased greatly!"

Judge Kane interrupted. "John, let's continue with the swearing in. Please raise your right hand and place your left hand on the Bible. Do you swear to tell the truth, the whole truth, and nothing but the truth, so help you God?"

"Well, of course, I do. Why would I not tell the truth?"

"You may continue, Mr. Stuart."

"Thank you, Your Honor. John, what is your occupation?"

"I am a fisherman by trade."

"Were you also a follower of the man known as Jesus Christ?"

"Yes. There were originally twelve of us in our group."

"John, it has been said you were one of the closest to Him in the group. Is that correct?"

"Well, perhaps. Jesus did spend a lot of his time with James, Peter, and me."

"Please tell us, John: After Jesus died on the cross, did you ever see Him again?"

"Oh yes, we did! He appeared to us many times over the next forty days."[4]

"So, are you saying that after He died, Jesus came back to life and appeared to you and others several times?"

"Yes!"

"That must have been absolutely incredible. Will you please give us an example of a specific time when you saw Him after He came back to life?"

"Yes, of course. A few days after He died, He appeared to me and the other disciples in the upper room. We saw the scars on His hands and in His side. However, Thomas was not with us when Jesus arrived."[5]

"Then what happened?"

John continued, "Eight days later, we were all together in a locked room. Jesus came and stood among us. This time, Thomas was with us, and he believed, too."[6]

"You stated that you saw Jesus many times after He came back to life. Will you please give us another example?"

"Yes, of course. One night we were fishing on the Sea of Tiberias—Simon Peter, Thomas, me, and a few others. We fished all night and didn't catch anything. When we were getting close to shore in the morning, we saw a man on the beach who called to us saying, 'Did you catch anything?' We said no, and He told us to throw our net on the right side of the boat. Soon our net was full of fish, and we knew it was the Lord who was waiting for us on shore."[7]

"John, some people in this courtroom may not have ever heard this before, and it may sound hard to believe. So, once again, for their benefit, are you saying Jesus died and three days later He came back to life?"

"Yes, that is correct."

"You are also telling us that He appeared to your group of disciples, as well as many other people, many times, for approximately forty days after He came back to life?"

"Yes. Yes!"

Oliver continued: "In fact, ladies and gentlemen of the jury, according to Paul, Jesus appeared to more than five hundred people at one time.[8] John, I can tell you are excited about this. Will you please tell the jury what happened when Jesus ascended into heaven for the final time?"

"Yes, of course. The other disciples and I were together when it happened. Jesus told us to wait in Jerusalem, that we would receive power when the Holy Spirit came upon us, and that we would be His witnesses in Jerusalem, in all Judea and Samaria, and to the end of the earth. Then He was lifted up into the air, and a cloud took Him out of our sight."[9]

"Then what happened?"

"Two men in white robes appeared to us and told us that when Jesus returns, He will come in the same way as we saw Him go into heaven."[10]

"These two men in white robes, they told you that when Jesus comes back, He will come the same way He left?"

"Yes."

"And you said that when He left, you saw Him leave the earth and go up into the clouds?"

"Yes."

"Just to clarify one more time: All these times you saw Him were after He had already died on the cross and rose from the dead. Correct?"

"Yes."

"Were there any other times you saw Him after he ascended into heaven?"

"Yes! I'm glad you asked that question. Many, many years later, as a very old man—well, as you see me today—I was sent to prison on the island of Patmos because of my faith.[11] It was during my time there that I saw Jesus again. He appeared to me and showed me things that were going to happen in the future, and He told me to write them down."

"John, we need to know more about the seven trumpets that Jesus told you about when you were exiled on the island of Patmos. Paul told us earlier on the witness stand that we become immortal *in the twinkling of an eye* at the last trumpet. For now, John, I would like us to focus on the sixth trumpet. Please explain to us what happens when the sixth angel blows his trumpet."

"Well, I'm afraid it's not good news. When the sixth angel blows his trumpet, one-third of the people on the earth are going to die."

"Are you certain about this?"

"Yes, I am sure."

"Your Honor, I would like to present to the jury the apostle John's detailed written account of the sixth trumpet, pointing out what looks to be a description of a war starting from the Euphrates River area. He gives the exact number of troops involved, 200 million, and as he said, the result of this event will be the death of one-third of the people on the earth."

"Very well, counselor, you may proceed."

"Thank you, Your Honor."

"Ladies and gentlemen of the jury, please refer to your exhibit binder at this time. Exhibit 4."

"John, will you please read for the court Exhibit 4, Revelation 9:13-18."

"Yes, of course, this is the revelation Jesus gave to me while I was a prisoner on Patmos. He told me to write the things I had seen, to write the things that are, and to write the things that will happen in the future."[12] John proceeded to read the exhibit aloud.

Exhibit 4
Revelation 9:13-18 (ESV)

"13Then the sixth angel blew his trumpet, and I heard a voice from the four horns of the golden altar before God, 14saying to the sixth angel who had the trumpet, 'Release the four angels who are bound at **the great river Euphrates.**' 15So the four angels, who had been prepared for the hour, the day, the month, and the year, were released to kill a third of mankind. 16The **number of mounted troops was twice ten thousand times ten thousand**; I heard their number. 17And this is how I saw the horses in my vision and those who rode them: they wore breastplates the color of fire and of sapphire and of sulfur, and the heads of the horses were like lions' heads, and fire and smoke and sulfur came out of their mouths. 18By these three plagues **a third of mankind was killed,** by the fire and smoke and sulfur coming out of their mouths."

"Thank you, John." Oliver said. He turned to the jury, continuing his argument. "Ladies and gentlemen, logic dictates that trumpets one through six must occur before the seventh trumpet. Since Paul explained, and I quote, 'We shall all be changed, in a moment, in the twinkling of an eye, at the *last* trumpet. For the trumpet will sound, and the dead will be raised imperishable, and we shall be changed,' we can conclude that the rapture *cannot happen* until the sixth trumpet has blown, which will result in the death of one-third of the people on earth.

"Your Honor, jury members, and guests of the court, so far in our proceedings today, we have identified five things that must occur before we are caught up to meet the Lord in the air, and we have proved conclusively that the rapture happens at the last trumpet." Oliver turned to the screen, reading out the following events that were listed for everyone to see:

1. *Falling away / Rebellion.*
2. *Temple built.*
3. *Antichrist revealed. He sits in the temple and claims to be God.*
4. *Christians who have already died rise first.*
5. *Sixth trumpet.*

Chapter 9

The Two Witnesses

N ext, Oliver wanted to switch gears and connect the Two Witnesses to the dead in Christ. He said, "Now, I would like to focus on number four on that list: 'Christians who have already died will rise first.' John, let's take a closer look at the two men you describe as the Two Witnesses." He turned to the judge. "At this time, Your Honor, with your permission, I would like to direct the jurors to Exhibit 5."

"Very well, counselor, you may proceed."

"Thank you, Your Honor.

"John, will you please read aloud the words God gave you to write; the words Jesus revealed to you on the island of Patmos?"

"Certainly," John said, and he began to read for the courtroom.

Exhibit 5
Revelation 11:1-15 (ESV)

"¹Then I was given a measuring rod like a staff, and I was told, 'Rise and measure the temple of God and the altar and those who worship there, ²but do not measure the court outside the temple; leave that out, for it is given over to the nations, and they will trample the holy city for forty-two months. ³And I will grant authority to my two witnesses, and they will prophesy for 1,260 days, clothed in sackcloth.'

⁴These are the two olive trees and the two lampstands that stand before the Lord of the earth. ⁵And if anyone would harm them, fire pours from their mouth and consumes their foes. If anyone would harm them, this is how he is doomed to be killed. ⁶They have the power to shut the sky, that no rain may fall during the days of their prophesying, and they have power over the waters to turn them into blood and to strike the earth with every kind of plague, as often as they desire.

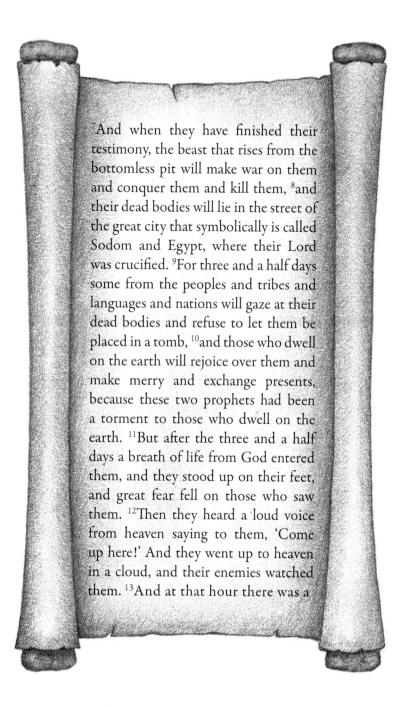

7And when they have finished their testimony, the beast that rises from the bottomless pit will make war on them and conquer them and kill them, 8and their dead bodies will lie in the street of the great city that symbolically is called Sodom and Egypt, where their Lord was crucified. 9For three and a half days some from the peoples and tribes and languages and nations will gaze at their dead bodies and refuse to let them be placed in a tomb, 10and those who dwell on the earth will rejoice over them and make merry and exchange presents, because these two prophets had been a torment to those who dwell on the earth. 11But after the three and a half days a breath of life from God entered them, and they stood up on their feet, and great fear fell on those who saw them. 12Then they heard a loud voice from heaven saying to them, 'Come up here!' And they went up to heaven in a cloud, and their enemies watched them. 13And at that hour there was a

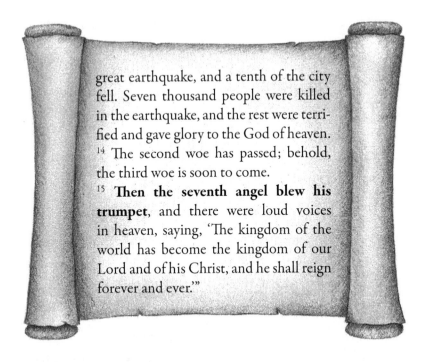

great earthquake, and a tenth of the city fell. Seven thousand people were killed in the earthquake, and the rest were terrified and gave glory to the God of heaven. [14] The second woe has passed; behold, the third woe is soon to come. [15] **Then the seventh angel blew his trumpet**, and there were loud voices in heaven, saying, 'The kingdom of the world has become the kingdom of our Lord and of his Christ, and he shall reign forever and ever.'"

"Thank you, John," Oliver said. "You have given us a lot of details. I have summarized them on the screen." He pointed to the list on the screen.

The Two Witnesses:

1. *Have authority and prophesy for 1,260 days.*
2. *Are killed by the Antichrist after 1,260 days.*
3. *Their dead bodies will lay in the street for three-and-a-half days.*
4. *People all over the world will be excited about this and give gifts to each other.*

5. *After being dead for three-and-a-half days, God raises them from the dead.*
6. *They stand up on their feet.*
7. *They hear a loud voice from heaven saying to them, 'Come up here!'*
8. *They ascend up to heaven in a cloud.*

"Ladies and gentlemen of the jury, I would like to draw your attention to number eight on the list: 'they ascend up to heaven in a cloud.' The word rapture is often defined as being caught up or ascending. When we examine the timing and surrounding events of the Two Witnesses ascending to heaven in a cloud, we have compelling evidence for the precise timing of the rapture. I will expand on this in a minute.

"John, you also wrote in verse 13 that four things will happen at the same time that the Two Witnesses ascend up into heaven in a cloud. Please tell us what these are."

"Certainly, Mr. Stuart. First, there will be a great earthquake. Second, a tenth of Jerusalem will fall in the earthquake. Third, seven thousand people will die as a result of this catastrophe. Fourth, those who do not die will be terrified and give glory to God."

"What happens after that, John?"

"The seventh angel blows his trumpet, and the kingdoms of this world become the kingdoms of our Lord and of his Christ, and he shall reign forever and ever."[1]

"John, is this when Jesus Christ returns to the earth, when the seventh trumpet blows?

"Yes."

"Thank you, John. I would like to remind everyone on the jury that Paul testified the rapture happens at the last trumpet,[2] a very specific point in time. John just told us that Jesus Christ returns at the seventh trumpet, which is the last trumpet." Turning to the Judge, Oliver said, "Your Honor, I have no further questions for this witness at this time."

Judge Kane dismissed John.

"Now," Oliver said, "I am going to explain the connection between the dead in Christ rising first[3] and the story of the Two Witnesses and how this connection gives us insight as to the probable timing of the rapture. Your Honor, again I ask for leniency."

Judge Kane responded, "Very well. Proceed, counselor."

Oliver referred the courtroom to Revelation 11:1-15. "The passage John just read tells us that the seventh trumpet happens right *after* the Two Witnesses are raptured or right after they 'ascend up to heaven in a cloud.' We know they are mortal beings, otherwise, they would not be able to die. We know they are going to die and lie in the street for three-and-a-half days.

"Once they die, the Two Witnesses become part of the group Paul described as 'the dead in Christ,' or Christians who have already died. Therefore, we know that when the Two Witnesses are raptured, the rest of the 'dead in Christ,' or Christians who have already died, will also be raptured.

"After that, the believers who are still alive at the time will be 'caught up,' or raptured, because Paul said 'the dead in Christ will rise first. Then we who are alive, who are left, will be caught up together with them in the clouds to meet the Lord in the air.'[4] So, I propose to you, ladies and gentlemen, that the rapture will either happen at the same time, or right after the Two Witnesses are raised from the dead." Oliver looked out at those assembled in the courtroom and then turned back to the judge. "At this time, Your Honor, I would like to request that everyone please reread 1 Thessalonians 4:15-17, Exhibit 6, a portion of Scripture from our earlier witness, the apostle Paul."

"Very well, counselor, proceed."

"Thank you, Your Honor. I have it up on the screen." Oliver read the exhibit aloud.

Exhibit 6
1 Thessalonians 4:15-17 (ESV)

"¹⁵For this we declare to you by a word from the Lord, that we who are alive, who are left until the coming of the Lord, will not precede those who have fallen asleep. ¹⁶For the Lord himself will descend from heaven with a cry of command, with the voice of an archangel, and with the sound of the trumpet of God. **And the dead in Christ will rise first.** ¹⁷**Then we who are alive, who are left, will be caught up together with them** in the clouds to meet the Lord in the air, and so we will always be with the Lord."

"Everyone," Oliver said, "please look at verse 16, where it says, 'the Lord himself will descend from heaven.' Remember what John told us earlier—that when Jesus ascended into heaven, the two men in white robes who appeared to the disciples said, 'When Jesus comes back, He is coming the same way He left, through the clouds.' Verses 16 and 17 say that (1) the Lord descends from heaven with the sound of a trumpet, (2) the dead in Christ will rise first, and (3) we who are left will be caught up together with them in the clouds to meet the Lord in the air.

"I draw your attention again to the screen. I have summarized the pieces of the puzzle and how they prove that the rapture cannot happen tomorrow, next week, next month or even next year because the Two Witnesses have not yet arrived on the world scene." He read the points listed aloud.

1. *The rapture happens at the last trumpet. Paul said, "Behold! I tell you a mystery. We shall not all sleep, but we shall all be changed, in a moment, in the twinkling of an eye, **at the last trumpet**. For the trumpet will sound, and the dead will be raised imperishable, and we shall be changed" (1 Corinthians 15:51-52).*

"Notice, please," Oliver said before continuing with the listed points, "it does not say we will disappear." He looked back to the remaining points.

2. *The seventh and last trumpet happens right after the Two Witnesses ascend into heaven in a cloud (Revelation 11:15).*

"It's logical," Oliver emphasized to the jury, "that once they die, the Two Witnesses become part of the group Paul described as 'the dead in Christ,' or Christians who have already died."

3. *Paul said, "the dead in Christ will rise first." So, the Two Witnesses must die first, then rise, before "we who are alive, who are left, will be caught up together with them in the clouds to meet the Lord in the air" (1 Thessalonians 4:16-17).*

Oliver summarized. "As you can see here, ladies and gentlemen, the Bible is very clear about the timing of the rapture. When we combine the writings of Paul and John, we don't have to guess or wonder when we will be changed in the twinkling of an eye."

Chapter 10

No One Knows the Day or the Hour

Now everyone who was convinced of a pre-tribulation rapture was getting a little upset. Oliver had just claimed to know the precise timing of the rapture. He could sense some resistance growing among the people.

"Now that I have established my arguments for a post-tribulation rapture," he said, "I would like to address a common objection to this view. I know you were all tracking with Holly when she made her case according to Scripture that 'no one knows the day or the hour.'[1] I agree with Holly, ladies and gentlemen, this is true—as of today. Today, none of us knows the day or the hour when Christ will come back and rapture His church. However, as the time gets closer, we *will* know because we will have seen the events happen that must happen before the rapture, one of which is the dead in Christ rising first. Remember, the Two Witnesses (1) prophesy for 1,260 days, (2) die, and (3) are 'raptured' three-and-a-half days after they die.

"So, even though we don't know *today* when the rapture will happen, we will know we are getting closer when the Two Witnesses arrive on the world scene. By the way, it will be easy to identify them. The Bible says they will destroy their enemies with fire from their mouths and they will have power to shut up the sky so that it will not rain during the days of their prophesying.[2] Also, they will be able to turn the waters into blood and to strike the earth with every kind of plague as often as they want.[3]

"We know the rapture will happen three-and-a-half days after the Two Witnesses are killed because Paul tells us the dead in Christ will rise first. 'Then we who are alive, who are left, will be caught up together with them' (1 Thessalonians 4:16-17).

"Ladies and gentlemen of the jury," Oliver continued, "if you want to examine the entire thirteenth chapter of the Gospel of Mark, you will see in verse 23 Jesus telling His disciples, 'But be on guard; **I have told you all things beforehand.**' In context, He is talking about the end-time events. First, He says He has told them everything in advance regarding the end times. Then He says, 'But concerning that day or that hour, no one knows, not even the angels in heaven, nor the Son, but only the Father.'[4]

"Since we know Jesus would not contradict himself, we can say without a doubt that both statements are true. Today, no one knows the day or the hour. There is enough information provided in the Bible, however, that when we take all the prophecies and put them together, we will know when the rapture will happen *as the time gets closer* and the prophesied events are being fulfilled."

Judge Kane raised his gavel and announced, "Court is now in recess. We will reconvene at 9:00 a.m. tomorrow. Counselors, I would like to see you in my chambers."

The time-traveling crew returned with the Bible men to the homestead and began preparing dinner. Ben and Amy hung back and waited for the attorneys to find out what the judge was concerned about.

Looking at Oliver, Judge Kane said, "Mr. Stuart, Do you plan to continue this charade throughout the entire trial?"

Oliver did not know how to answer. He was stuck. If he told the truth, that there really was a time machine and that they just met the real Paul and John, they would not believe him. If he tried to convince them, that could potentially put Ben's and Amy's careers in jeopardy.

"Your Honor, I do plan to bring two more witnesses from the Bible. Do you see any harm in me doing so?"

Judge Kane looked at Holly. "Ms. Norton, you brought several Bible prophecy experts to the stand to support your case. Do you have any objections to Mr. Stuart continuing with his actors?"

Holly replied, "No objections, Your Honor. As long as they are quoting or confirming the Scriptures, I'm fine with that. I'm confident that I convinced everyone in town that the rapture can happen at any time; today, tomorrow, next week, or whenever God wants."

"Very well," Judge Kane continued. "We will, however, discontinue the swearing-in process. I am not going to have these people placing their hands on the Bible stating that they are telling the whole truth and nothing but the truth when, in fact, they are not who they say they are. One more thing, will you please ask the men to speak English? Then we don't have to wear these uncomfortable things in our ears."

Oliver answered, "Well, Your Honor, they do not understand or speak any English. So, to continue, we will have to use the translation devices to communicate."

Judge Kane looked at him in disbelief and said, "Seriously?"

"I'm afraid so, Your Honor."

"Very well. That is all. You are dismissed."

As they walked out together, Holly said, "You're kidding, right? They don't speak English? What's up with that?"

Oliver said, "I'm not kidding, Holly, and I want you to watch them carefully and continually. Don't take your eyes off them. Listen to them when they are not on the stand and pay attention to how they interact with each other."

"Why? What for? What's up with you anyway? You are not acting like yourself."

This whole situation was driving Oliver nuts. He wanted his sister and his parents to know that these men were the real deal. They were missing an opportunity of a lifetime, and once they found out the truth, they were going to be disappointed for not knowing sooner.

Oliver answered, "It's complicated, Holly. I'll see you in the morning."

Chapter 11

What Event Will Start the Final Seven Years?

More townspeople showed up on Thursday morning, even people who didn't attend church or read the Bible. Word had spread that Oliver was bringing in actors who didn't speak English and were dressed in costumes to play the parts of Bible characters.

"Mr. Stuart, are you ready to begin today's session?" asked Judge Kane.

"Yes, Your Honor."

"Very well then, you may proceed."

"Thank you, Your Honor. Ladies and gentlemen, yesterday, I believe I proved to you the timing of the rapture. Now we are going to shift our focus a bit and examine the sequence of events leading up to the rapture of the church. Today, I am calling to the stand a very special guest from the Old Testament to help us with this. I present to you the prophet Daniel."

People in the courtroom started taking pictures of Daniel

as he walked up to the witness stand. Many of them had grown up hearing the story of how he survived the night in the lion's den because of God's protection.[1] They remembered his friends too: Hananiah, Mishael, and Azariah, otherwise known as Shadrach, Meshach, and Abednego, and how God delivered them unharmed from the fiery furnace because they did not worship the golden image King Nebuchadnezzar had set up.[2]

Oliver turned to the stand. "Daniel, welcome to our town. We are honored to have you as our guest today. We have brought you from your time to approximately 2,500 years into the future."

Daniel responded in Hebrew: "הדות .הזה ווייסינל רחביהל דובכ הז ואכל יתוא תאיבהש."

The judge, a few jurors, and several court guests fumbled to put in their translation devices because they could not understand him. The Convers8 devices translated Daniel's speech: "It is an honor to be chosen for this experience. Thank you for bringing me here."

When everyone had their TDs in place, Oliver addressed Daniel. "We have been studying what you wrote and how God communicates with you through dreams. For example, the time God revealed to you King Nebuchadnezzar's dream and its interpretation.[3]

"It is also clear in your writings, Daniel, that God chose you to write specific things that are going to happen in the future, in the time of the end.[4] Many of the people in our town believe we are the ones living in the end time, or at the end of the age. Since God told you things that are going to happen in the future, we have brought you here today to gain more insight about what you wrote more than 2,500 years ago regarding the final seven years."

Daniel responded, "Yes. I am happy to be here, experience your culture, taste your food, and see future advancements. What are those objects many are wearing over their eyes?"

Oliver answered, "They are called eyeglasses, or simply, glasses. They help us see better. Some people need them to see things in the distance and some need them to read words up close."

Daniel asks, "How can they do both at the same time?"

"Well, Daniel, honestly, I am not an expert in eyeglasses, so that would be hard for me to answer."

Judge Kane interjected, "Counselor, please ask your witness a question."

"Yes, Your Honor. Daniel, what event will start the final seven years?"

Daniel pondered for a few seconds before he answered. "The event that starts the final seven years will be the Confirmation of the Covenant.[5] Has that happened yet?"

"Daniel, are you referring to the covenant that God originally made with Abraham,[6] promising land to him and his descendants forever?"

"Yes, that is correct. The covenant God made with Abraham."

"No, Daniel, the Confirmation of the Covenant has not happened yet."

"Are not Abraham's descendants living in the promised land in the future?"

"Yes, they are. But there is a problem."

"What seems to be the problem?"

Oliver explained, "It is true, many of Abraham's descendants are living in the promised land, known today as Israel. However, twenty of the twenty-two Arab countries in the Middle East region do not currently recognize Israel's right to exist.*,7

"Since the majority of the countries do not recognize the Jewish people's right to a homeland in the Holy Land, we are waiting for the confirmation of Abraham's covenant. Or, in other words, we are waiting for the world leaders to recognize this promise from God that Israel does have a right to a homeland." Oliver turned to the jury. "Daniel has just told us the event that starts the final seven years will be the Confirmation of the Covenant." Looking to the judge, he continued. "Your Honor, I do not plan to bring Moses to the witness stand, and since the two rapture camps agree that Moses wrote the book of Genesis, will you please allow me to examine a small portion of his writing to define 'the covenant' which Daniel is referring to?"

"As you wish, Mr. Stuart."

"Thank you, Your Honor."

---

* These twenty Arab countries are continually threatening to destroy Israel. Israel would like to negotiate a peace agreement so that all can live in peace and not feel as though they are under continual threat.

Oliver directed his next comments to the jury. "At this time, please refer to Exhibits 7 and 8. These are passages from the Old Testament book of Genesis, written by Moses. The Scriptures describe the promise God gave to Abraham, that he and his descendants will own a specific piece of property. You will also see the passage describe the borders from the river of Egypt to the great river Euphrates." He read the exhibits aloud.

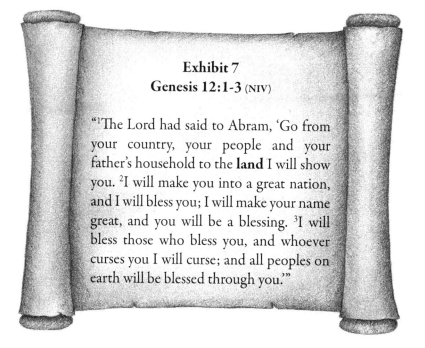

Exhibit 7
Genesis 12:1-3 (NIV)

"¹The Lord had said to Abram, 'Go from your country, your people and your father's household to the **land** I will show you. ²I will make you into a great nation, and I will bless you; I will make your name great, and you will be a blessing. ³I will bless those who bless you, and whoever curses you I will curse; and all peoples on earth will be blessed through you.'"

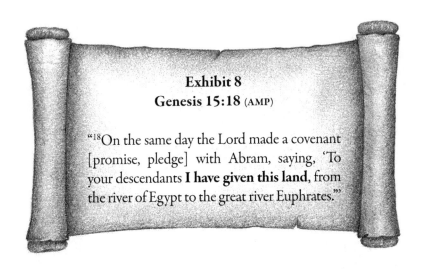

Exhibit 8
Genesis 15:18 (AMP)

"[18]On the same day the Lord made a covenant [promise, pledge] with Abram, saying, 'To your descendants **I have given this land**, from the river of Egypt to the great river Euphrates.'"

"According to Moses," Oliver continued, "God promised land to Abraham and his descendants. We know this because Abraham left the city of Haran with his wife, his nephew Lot, all their possessions, and the people who were with them. God told him to 'Go from your country . . . to the land I will show you.' When they got to the land, the Lord appeared to Abraham and said, 'To your offspring I will give this land.'[8] Now we will move on to examine more closely what God told Daniel regarding the future and the confirmation of this covenant."

Chapter 12

The Confirmation of the Covenant

"Daniel, we know you wrote in Aramaic and in Hebrew. As was mentioned earlier in our proceedings, the Bible, which includes what you wrote, has now been translated into more than 700 languages. In our English language alone, there are numerous translations of what you wrote. Some of the well-known translations are the King James Version (KJV), the New International Version (NIV), the English Standard Version (ESV), and the Amplified Version (AMP).

"Your Honor, I have entered into evidence Daniel's writings regarding the Confirmation of the Covenant, Exhibit 9, words he wrote more than 2,500 years ago. According to Daniel 9:27, an event that confirms a covenant will start the clock ticking on the final seven years.

"I have it available here in four different translations in the exhibit binders for our jurors to compare. Examining the same passage in each translation will provide a clear, combined explanation of the event that happens at the beginning of the final seven years. In addition, in this same verse, Daniel also explains to us what will happen in the middle of the seven years. Your Honor, may I present this evidence at this time?"

"Yes, please continue, counselor."

"Thank you, Your Honor.

"Daniel, please read your writing aloud for us, Exhibit 9."

"Certainly."

Daniel read aloud from the iPad in Hebrew, "תִיךְב רִיבְגֵהְו
דַעו, םֵמֹשְׁמ סִיצּוּקִשׁ ףַנְכ לַעְו, הָחְנְמוּ. חַבֶז תִיבְשִׁי_עוּבָּשֵׁ יֶצָחוֹ; דָחֶא_עוּבָשׁ, סִיבַּרְל
‎ .{פ}. מֵמֹשׁ-לַע ךֶתֶּת, הָצָרֵחֶנְו ךֶלֵכ‎"

The same passage was provided in four different translations in the exhibit binders and on the screen for everyone to compare.

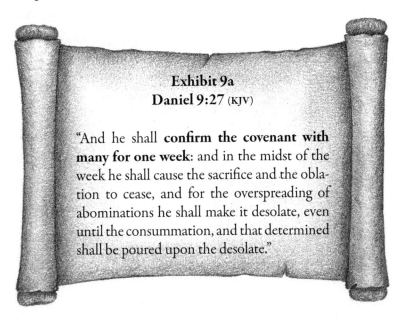

Exhibit 9a
Daniel 9:27 (KJV)

"And he shall **confirm the covenant with many for one week**: and in the midst of the week he shall cause the sacrifice and the oblation to cease, and for the overspreading of abominations he shall make it desolate, even until the consummation, and that determined shall be poured upon the desolate."

Exhibit 9b
Daniel 9:27 (NIV)

"He will **confirm a covenant with many for one 'seven.'** In the middle of the 'seven' he will put an end to sacrifice and offering. And at the temple he will set up an abomination that causes desolation, until the end that is decreed is poured out on him."

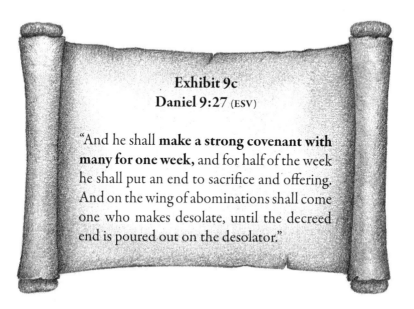

Exhibit 9c
Daniel 9:27 (ESV)

"And he shall **make a strong covenant with many for one week,** and for half of the week he shall put an end to sacrifice and offering. And on the wing of abominations shall come one who makes desolate, until the decreed end is poured out on the desolator."

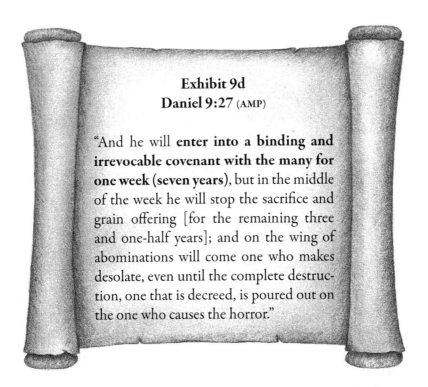

Exhibit 9d
Daniel 9:27 (AMP)

"And he will **enter into a binding and irrevocable covenant with the many for one week (seven years)**, but in the middle of the week he will stop the sacrifice and grain offering [for the remaining three and one-half years]; and on the wing of abominations will come one who makes desolate, even until the complete destruction, one that is decreed, is poured out on the one who causes the horror."

"Now," Oliver continued, "I would like everyone to focus on that first line." He pointed to the screen, where each version of the line was displayed.

- *(KJV) "And he shall confirm the covenant with many **for one week**."*
- *(NIV) "He will confirm a covenant with many **for one 'seven.'**"*
- *(ESV) "And he shall make a strong covenant with many **for one week**."*
- *(AMP) "And he will enter into a binding and irrevocable covenant with the many **for one week (seven years)**."*

"Each translation mentions the time period of one week or one 'seven,' indicating a temporary covenant, lasting only seven years. Both pre-tribulation and post-tribulation camps agree that this is a seven-year period. Two translations state that the covenant will be confirmed. The other two state that someone will 'make a strong covenant' or 'enter into a binding and irrevocable covenant.' It is implied that the covenant will be confirmed at the beginning of the seven years.

"I propose to you, ladies and gentlemen of the jury, that a Middle East peace agreement between Israel and the Palestinians confirming Israel's right to exist will mark the beginning of the final seven years, and is, in fact, the same event that Daniel is referring to as the Confirmation of the Covenant.

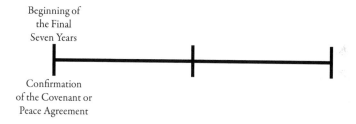

Beginning of
the Final
Seven Years

Confirmation
of the Covenant or
Peace Agreement

"Now let us move on to the middle of the final seven years, again in the same passage, Daniel 9:27. Notice that the NIV translation says, 'In the middle of the "seven," he will put an end to sacrifice and offering. And at the temple, he will set up an abomination that causes desolation, until the end that is decreed is poured out on him.'" Oliver looked at Daniel. "So,

Daniel, are you saying that in the middle of the seven years is an event called the Abomination of Desolation?"

Daniel said, "Yes, that is correct."

Oliver asked, "What does that mean?"

"It means that the armed forces of the leader will desecrate the temple and stop animal sacrifices in the middle of the final seven years."

Oliver, speaking to the jury, said, "Ladies and gentlemen, I have that documented for you in your binders: Exhibit 10a-d; Daniel 11:31 for you to examine."

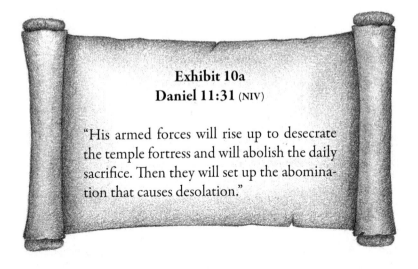

Exhibit 10a
Daniel 11:31 (NIV)

"His armed forces will rise up to desecrate the temple fortress and will abolish the daily sacrifice. Then they will set up the abomination that causes desolation."

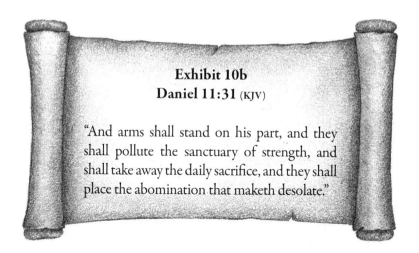

Exhibit 10b
Daniel 11:31 (KJV)

"And arms shall stand on his part, and they shall pollute the sanctuary of strength, and shall take away the daily sacrifice, and they shall place the abomination that maketh desolate."

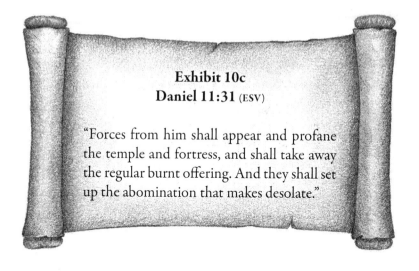

Exhibit 10c
Daniel 11:31 (ESV)

"Forces from him shall appear and profane the temple and fortress, and shall take away the regular burnt offering. And they shall set up the abomination that makes desolate."

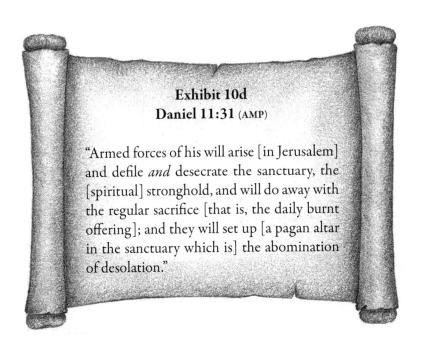

Exhibit 10d
Daniel 11:31 (AMP)

"Armed forces of his will arise [in Jerusalem] and defile *and* desecrate the sanctuary, the [spiritual] stronghold, and will do away with the regular sacrifice [that is, the daily burnt offering]; and they will set up [a pagan altar in the sanctuary which is] the abomination of desolation."

"Thank you, Daniel. And thank you for being with us today and being one of our special guests. We appreciate your testimony."

"Thank you very much. It was my pleasure to be of service."

"Your Honor, I have no further questions for this witness." The judge dismissed Daniel and Oliver continued talking. "Ladies and gentlemen of the jury, Daniel is telling us that once the Confirmation of the Covenant, or peace agreement, happens, three-and-a-half years later, an event called the Abomination of Desolation will occur. We will recognize it because we will be watching our calendars for the three-and-a-half-year mark. The other way we will recognize this event is that someone, "he," is going to stop the daily sacrifice and offering in a newly built temple. Now we need to know what sacrifices and offerings are going to be stopped, and who is going to stop them.

"Just to remind everyone," Oliver said, "on day one of our proceedings, our first witness was the apostle Paul. He provided evidence stating the rapture cannot happen until the Antichrist stands in the temple or 'takes his seat in the temple of God, proclaiming himself to be God.'[1] He gave a very specific description, proving it is the Antichrist who will stand on the Temple Mount. Since there is not currently a Jewish Temple on the Temple Mount in Israel, I argued that a third temple will need to be built. Once the temple is built, the Jewish people will resume animal sacrifices as they did in the Old Testament, offered as an atonement for sins. These are the sacrifices that will be stopped in the middle of the final seven years.

"We will recognize the 'he' as the Antichrist when he stops the resumed animal sacrifices on the Temple Mount in Jerusalem, three-and-a-half years after the Confirmation of the Covenant.

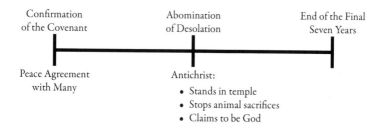

"Ladies and gentlemen, I have Exhibit 9b on the screen for you to reread."

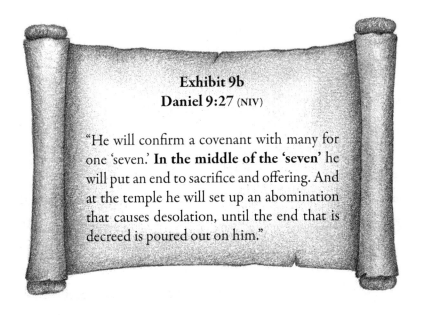

Exhibit 9b
Daniel 9:27 (NIV)

"He will confirm a covenant with many for one 'seven.' **In the middle of the 'seven' he will put an end to sacrifice and offering.** And at the temple he will set up an abomination that causes desolation, until the end that is decreed is poured out on him."

Oliver continued, "So, once again, according to Daniel, the Abomination of Desolation is an event that will happen in the middle of the final seven years. The Antichrist will stop the animal sacrifices on the Temple Mount, and according to the apostle Paul in 2 Thessalonians 2:1-4, he will also proclaim himself to be God."

At this time, Judge Kane interrupted, raising his hand with the gavel and announcing, "I think you have made your point. We will break now and reconvene at 1 p.m."

During the break, many of the townspeople ate their picnic lunches on the lawn in front of the courthouse. Holly sat with her family and her parents, strategically placing her blanket as close as she could to Paul, John, Daniel, and the fourth witness who had not yet been introduced. She kept her TDs in her ears and faced the opposite direction so as not to appear like she was trying to eavesdrop. She thought to herself, "They never go out of character. They never speak English, they break bread and pray, the way I've seen in those Bible movies, and they act as if they have never seen so many things. The costumes look like they were made just for them, are very out of the ordinary, and have a strong, unpleasant odor." She was suspicious of Oliver and these men. She suspected that Oliver and Amy were keeping some sort of secret. And why were Ben and a few of his friends hanging around all week? That, in and of itself, was highly unusual. She also couldn't figure out why her brother would spend so much money to hire these people. She was determined to figure out what was really going on.

Chapter 13

The Middle East Peace Agreement

A fter lunch, the bailiff announced that court was reconvening, and Oliver continued presenting his case. "Your Honor, I call Dr. Sarah Anderson to the stand."

"Very well, counselor, please continue."

"Dr. Anderson, thank you very much for being here today. Please tell the court where you live and what you do for a living."

Dr. Anderson replied, "I live here in Cherry Creek with my husband, and I work for the Institute for Advanced Prophetic Studies based out of Washington, DC."

"Please tell the jury, Dr. Anderson, what is the focus of the Institute for Advanced Prophetic Studies?"

"The institute is a think tank of sorts, funded by the government to advise heads of state in matters pertaining to current world events. We primarily focus on the different theories related to the sequence of 'end time' events according to the prophecies in the Bible. We interview numerous pastors and experts in the field. We study and cross-reference their theories. Many of the experts disagree on details, but they all pretty much agree that we are living in the end of time as we know it. The purpose of the Institute is to see what we can glean from Bible experts and their interpretations of the prophecies, to give us an advantage on the world stage in the times ahead."

"What is your title, or your position, at the institute, and what do you do there?"

"I am the director of research for the institute. I oversee two teams. One team researches what experts call a pre-tribulation rapture event, and my other team focuses on evidence supporting a post-tribulation rapture. For several years, I traveled the country attending various prophecy conferences and interviewing numerous pastors. I still travel some, but a lot of the conferences are now streamed. Some of the experts are also from other countries, including Israel. The institute has different divisions. My staff and I study the research and share our findings with the vice-chairman of the Joint Chiefs of Staff, headquartered at the Pentagon."

"Thank you, Dr. Anderson. We know Holly flew in people from your team to testify for the pre-tribulation position. Today, I have asked you here to represent your other team, the group that investigates the post-tribulation position. Out of all the post-tribulation experts your team has interviewed and studied, is there any one particular person who stands out above the others, and if so, why?"

"Well, actually, there is one particular pastor the team follows closely. His name is Irvin Baxter."

"According to the research, Dr. Anderson, what kind of credibility does Irvin Baxter bring to the table?"

"It's rather interesting," she answered. "He started teaching in 1968 that the Berlin Wall would come down one day."

"Did you say 1968?" Oliver questioned. "That's what, twenty-one years before the wall came down?"

"Correct. He didn't know when, but according to what he understood from the prophecies, he foretold that the Berlin Wall would be torn down, that East and West Germany would be reunited, and that these events would be the catalyst to propel the world into the New World Order."[1]

"Dr. Anderson, tell us: how did Pastor Baxter substantiate his teaching with proof?"

"Well, in 1986, three years before the wall came down, he published a book entitled *A Message for the President*. In his book, he explained the prophecy and how he identified the United States, Great Britain, Russia, and Germany in the Bible. When I interviewed him, he said his phone didn't stop ringing on the day the wall came down. Everyone was calling and asking how he knew in advance the wall was going to come down.[2] They wanted to know what was going to happen next."

"Did you ask him that question too?"

"I did!" Dr. Anderson replied.

"Before you continue, Dr. Anderson, I want to let the jury and townspeople know that I asked you to come today prepared with your notes on what Irvin Baxter is teaching and that you are free to refer to your notes when necessary. You may continue now. What did he say when you asked him what he thinks is coming soon?"

"Baxter teaches that the Confirmation of the Covenant that Daniel spoke of in Daniel 9:27 will present itself in the end time as a peace agreement between Israel and the Palestinians and that when it's signed, it is his opinion that the agreement will mark the beginning of the final seven years to the Battle of Armageddon and the physical return of Jesus Christ to the earth. He also teaches that the agreement must contain at least four specific elements to qualify as the agreement spoken of by the prophet."

"Dr. Anderson, please tell the court what those four elements are."

"Sure. Baxter's first element is that the coming peace agreement will establish the final borders of Israel, acknowledging Israel's right to exist. This will include the establishment of a Palestinian state in Judea, commonly known as the West Bank area.[3,4] Secondly, he believes it will allow the Jewish settlers currently living in the West Bank to continue living there, in their homes, as a Jewish minority in the new Palestinian state.[5,6] Third, he says it will place the Temple Mount under an internationally supervised sharing arrangement, allowing both Jews and Muslims to worship there.[7,8] Fourth, the agreement may not specifically say that a Jewish temple will be built. However, the Jewish people will likely not sign a final agreement that does not provide some kind of a path for them to rebuild their temple on the Temple Mount, which can be done without disturbing the Dome of the Rock or the Al-Aqsa Mosque."[9,10]

"Thank you, Dr. Anderson. Did Pastor Baxter also give you his opinion or any Scripture references to back up these four elements?"

"He did. Matthew 24:15-21 gives a description of those living in Judea having to run for their lives. They won't have time to go back into their houses to grab anything and take it with them. Verse 15 says this will happen at the time of the Abomination of Desolation, and verse 21 says this is when the Great Tribulation will start. In Baxter's opinion, there would be no reason for the Jewish settlers currently living in the West Bank area to have to run for their lives unless the Palestinians gain control of that area. This is why he is sure that there will be a Palestinian state created in Judea as part of the peace agreement. Also, it's logical then that the Jewish settlers currently living there will be allowed to stay in their current homes living as a Jewish minority in the new Palestinian state because it's not feasible to force approximately 500,000 Jews to leave their homes and relocate."

"Thank you, Dr. Anderson. Your Honor, I have entered this passage of Scripture into evidence for the jurors, so they can read along in their exhibit binders as I read it on the screen."

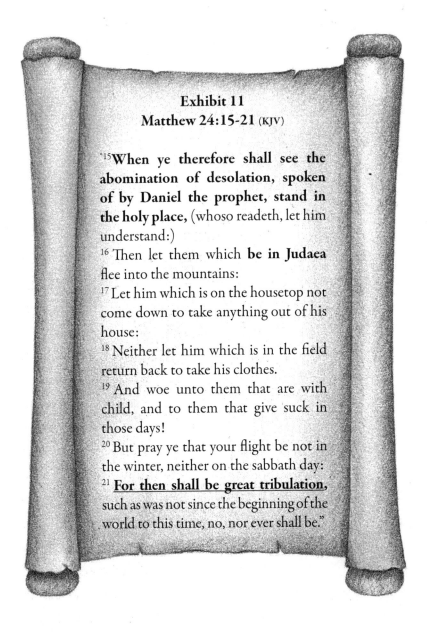

Exhibit 11
Matthew 24:15-21 (KJV)

"¹⁵**When ye therefore shall see the abomination of desolation, spoken of by Daniel the prophet, stand in the holy place,** (whoso readeth, let him understand:)

¹⁶ Then let them which **be in Judaea** flee into the mountains:

¹⁷ Let him which is on the housetop not come down to take anything out of his house:

¹⁸ Neither let him which is in the field return back to take his clothes.

¹⁹ And woe unto them that are with child, and to them that give suck in those days!

²⁰ But pray ye that your flight be not in the winter, neither on the sabbath day:

²¹ **For then shall be great tribulation,** such as was not since the beginning of the world to this time, no, nor ever shall be."

Oliver continued, "Dr. Anderson, how long have you worked for the Institute for Advanced Prophetic Studies?"

"I have been with the Institute for fifteen years. I started with the pre-tribulation research team. Then after about seven years, I was transferred over to the post-tribulation team. About three years ago, I was promoted to director."

"What is it that you like best about your job?"

Dr. Anderson responded, "Well, I have the privilege of talking to people all the time about the Bible and the prophecies. I get to meet new people and study what the different experts teach. I watch DVDs, listen to podcasts, watch online prophecy shows, read their books, magazines, and attend conferences. I think it's fascinating how the Bible foretells the future! I also find that knowing the prophecies creates a nice transition into a conversation about the gospel."

"Dr. Anderson, it sounds like you have spent about equal time studying each side of the debate. Why is it that you and your post-tribulation staff know so much about Irvin Baxter and what he teaches?"

"Well, two people on my team are enrolled in the Jerusalem Prophecy College in downtown Jerusalem. One lives in Jerusalem and the other lives here in the United States, completing his classes online. For me, personally, in addition to all my regular responsibilities with the institute, I listen to the *End of the Age* online daily show and have for many years. I also read *EndTime* magazine and have watched many of Irvin Baxter's DVDs. One highlight of my career was participating in an Israel tour sponsored by Endtime Ministries."

"Thank you, Dr. Anderson. Let's get back to the scripture

references Pastor Baxter uses to identify the required elements in the peace agreement for it to be considered the Confirmation of the Covenant spoken of by Daniel. You said, according to Baxter, the agreement will place the Temple Mount under an internationally supervised sharing arrangement allowing both Jews and Muslims to worship there. How does he know this?"

Dr. Anderson answered, "It's Baxter's opinion that the apostle John is painting us a picture in Revelation 11:1-2 of a temple under a sharing arrangement. Do you have the text available for the court?"

"Yes, we do. Your Honor, at this time I will read aloud Exhibit 12, Revelation 11:1-2. I have it up on the screen, and it is also included in the exhibit binder."

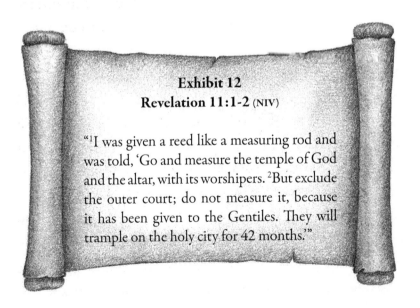

Exhibit 12
Revelation 11:1-2 (NIV)

"¹I was given a reed like a measuring rod and was told, 'Go and measure the temple of God and the altar, with its worshipers. ²But exclude the outer court; do not measure it, because it has been given to the Gentiles. They will trample on the holy city for 42 months.'"

"Please continue, Dr. Anderson. What does Baxter say about this?"

"Well, he says John was told to rise and measure the temple of God and the altar and those who worship there. But he was told not to measure the court outside the temple, leaving that part out because that part is given over to the nations. In other words, Baxter believes people from all nations will be able to visit and worship on the Temple Mount, in the outer court, for a period of 42 months. He says this scripture paints for us a picture of the Temple Mount being shared by both Muslims and Jews."

"Thank you, Dr. Anderson. Let's move on to Baxter's fourth criterion for how we will recognize the peace agreement, or the Confirmation of the Covenant, when we see it. You said the peace agreement will likely provide a path for the building of the third Jewish temple. How does Baxter know this?"

"Oh, this is very logical, and I agree with him. We know this because Paul said in 2 Thessalonians 2:4 that the Antichrist will sit in the temple, claiming to be God. The Antichrist can't sit in a temple if there isn't one for him to sit in. Daniel said this event is called the Abomination of Desolation and will happen in the middle of the final seven years."

"Thank you, Dr. Anderson. So, in your professional opinion, do you agree with Pastor Baxter that if a peace agreement happened next week, for example, that did not include these four criteria, we would not yet enter the final seven years?"

"Yes, that is my personal opinion."

"Ladies and gentlemen of the jury," Oliver continued, "I propose to you that we will know the final seven years have begun when we see the covenant God made with Abraham confirmed. There will be an agreement, or peace agreement, 'with many,' that recognizes Israel's right to a homeland. The phrase 'with many' indicates that several countries, or the leaders of several countries, will be in agreement. A Palestinian state will be established in Judea, allowing the current Jewish settlers permission to remain living there. The agreement will include the sharing of the Temple Mount between Jews and Muslims and will leave the door open for the third Jewish temple to be built on the Temple Mount. Further confirmation will come, of course, when the Jewish people begin building the temple." Oliver turned and addressed the stand, "Dr. Anderson, do you know if the status of Jerusalem will be finalized in the coming peace agreement?"

"I do not know, Mr. Stuart. However, Baxter teaches that the status of Jerusalem will be postponed. He believes they are not going to be able to resolve this issue and that Jerusalem will remain undivided under Israeli control. Neither the Palestinians nor the Israelis will be willing to surrender control over Jerusalem. Consequently, according to Baxter, they are going to say, 'Well, look, everything else is fixed, let's just put this contentious issue off—apparently for the next seven years.'"[11] Dr. Anderson referred to her notes and continued, "Let me quote Baxter. 'Both sides are saying 'No, we must have Jerusalem.' But before it's over with, the Palestinians are going to have to yield on that point, and Israel is going to keep Jerusalem, at least for a seven-year period, and that may be when the time frame is built-in—when they say, 'Okay, let's put this issue off. It's the one unsolvable issue. Let's put it off, and we'll bring it back seven years from now.' That's sort of the way I envision seeing it happen',[12] end quote."

"Another question for you, Dr. Anderson. When you interviewed Pastor Baxter, did he discuss with you his prediction for a time of great revival during the end time?"

"Yes, he did. In fact, he is predicting the greatest revival of all time."

"How exactly did he come to this understanding?"

"Well, bear with me as I read from my notes again. It's Baxter's opinion that the entire seventh chapter of the book of Revelation is devoted to foretelling a great end-time revival. Verses one through eight, he says, are devoted to the sealing of 144,000 Jews. It appears, according to his interpretation, that these will be born-again Jewish believers. Chapter seven also prophesies a great Gentile revival. Verse nine says, 'After this I beheld, and, lo, a great multitude, which no man could number, of all nations, and kindreds, and people, and tongues, stood before the throne, and before the Lamb, clothed with white robes, and palms in their hands.' According to Baxter, that's a lot of people. Do you want me to keep reading?"

"Yes, please continue."

"Irvin read to me verses 13 and 14. 'And one of the elders answered, saying unto me, What are these which are arrayed in white robes? and whence came they? And I said unto him, Sir, thou knowest. And he said to me, These are they which came out of great tribulation, and have washed their robes, and made them white in the blood of the Lamb.' He says this proves to us that there will be multitudes of people who are going to be saved 'in the blood of the Lamb' coming out of the tribulation period."

"Dr. Anderson, please restate those references in case anyone wants to write them down," Oliver said.

"Sure: Revelation 7:9 and Revelation 7:13-14, King James Version."

"Thank you, Dr. Anderson. So what you are telling us is that even though there is going to be great tribulation, this will also be a really exciting time, too, because the believers will be doing more evangelizing than ever before, and as a result, more people than ever will put their faith in Christ during this time period. Is that the official position of the Institute for Advanced Prophetic Studies?"

"That is Baxter's belief according to his understanding of the Scriptures. The institute itself does not take a position."

"Fair enough. One more question, Dr. Anderson. Do you know if Endtime Ministries has a plan in place for this end-time revival they are predicting?"

"Yes, actually they do. That's the interesting part. We haven't come across many other experts in the field who have an extensive plan and goals for the time ahead of us. Endtime Ministries has a plan to send an *EndTime* magazine to every single home in Israel, 2.4 million of them, when the peace agreement is signed. Their cover page is going to say: 'Warning: Final Seven Years Just Began, What To Do, See Inside.' They are going to craft the magazine to give this message to the Jewish people, believing that many of them will be a part of this great end-time revival in Israel. Irvin told me that when he looks forward to this final seven years, he's not looking forward to it with dread but with great anticipation. And he is gearing up to be ready to evangelize like he has never evangelized in his life."[13]

"Thank you, Dr. Anderson," Oliver said. "I also heard something about a door-knocking campaign in the West Bank area. What can you tell us about that?"

"I can only tell you what I've heard on the End of the Age broadcast," she said. "The ministry is organizing a strategic plan, inviting hundreds of qualified volunteers to go with them and knock on doors,[14] warning the Jewish people about the upcoming event known as the Abomination of Desolation. This will give them time to relocate, if they choose, to avoid having to run for their lives as Jesus describes in Matthew 24:15-21."

"Thank you for being with us today, Dr. Anderson. Your Honor, I have no more questions for this witness."

"Very well, counselor. Dr. Anderson, you may step down."

Chapter 14

When Did Jesus Say
He Will Return?

"Next, Your Honor, I would like to call another one of Jesus's disciples to the stand: Matthew."

"Very well, counselor, you may continue."

"A warm welcome to you this afternoon, Matthew," Oliver said. "It is a great honor to have you here with us today. We are taking an in-depth look at the final seven years. The people in our town believe we are living in the end times, and we brought you here today to ask you questions about what Jesus said. Since you spent so much time with Him, we have called you as an eyewitness to our courtroom today."

"Thank you, Mr. Stuart, for inviting me and for your hospitality. It's an honor to meet everyone, especially the prophet Daniel, and to be here in this time with John and Paul."

"Will you please share with us your occupation, Matthew?"

"I used to be a tax collector."

"Did you know Jesus Christ as a personal friend?"

"Yes. Jesus came up to me one day at the tax booth and said, 'Follow me.' So, I got up and followed Him."

"Is that when you officially became one of His disciples?"

"I suppose so, yes."

"So, once you started following Him, did you spend most of your time with Him from that point on?"

"Yes. I joined His group of followers and we spent approximately three years with Him until He was crucified on the cross at Calvary; then He came back to life after He died. It was incredible!"

"Your Honor, I would like to point out to the ladies and gentlemen of the jury that Matthew wrote about many of the events that took place during the life of Jesus, and they are written in *The Gospel According to Matthew*, which is included in the Bible. Being an eyewitness, Matthew was also able to record many of the things Jesus said, so we can quote His exact words today." Oliver turned to Matthew. "Matthew, our biggest question for you today is this: When will the rapture occur? Did Jesus ever tell you and the other disciples when He is coming back to gather the church?"

"Yes, certainly. I wrote that in my account. He is coming back immediately after the tribulation."

"Your Honor, I have included Matthew's exact text in the exhibit binders. I would like to examine Exhibit 13 at this time."

"Very well, counselor, you may proceed."

"Thank you, Your Honor," Oliver said. "Matthew, please read aloud to the court what you wrote while the jurors follow along in their exhibit binders. You may begin."

"Very well, Mr. Stuart," he said, and he began to read aloud.

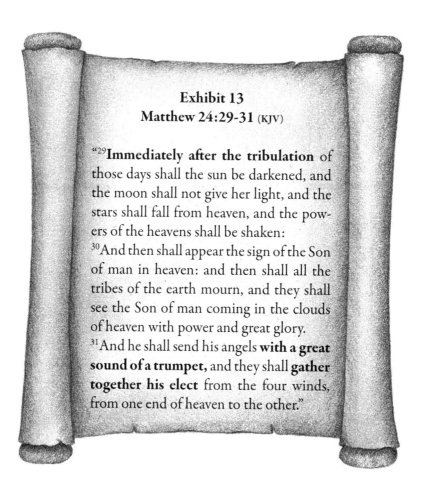

Exhibit 13
Matthew 24:29-31 (KJV)

"[29]**Immediately after the tribulation** of those days shall the sun be darkened, and the moon shall not give her light, and the stars shall fall from heaven, and the powers of the heavens shall be shaken:
[30]And then shall appear the sign of the Son of man in heaven: and then shall all the tribes of the earth mourn, and they shall see the Son of man coming in the clouds of heaven with power and great glory.
[31]And he shall send his angels **with a great sound of a trumpet,** and they shall **gather together his elect** from the four winds, from one end of heaven to the other."

"Thank you, Matthew. Do you remember where you were when Jesus said these words?"

"Yes, I was sitting on the Mount of Olives along with the other disciples. We asked Jesus, 'What will be the sign of your coming and of the close of the age?' This was part of the answer that He gave."

"Thank you, Matthew. Ladies and gentlemen of the jury, please notice verse 29. Jesus told His disciples that He is coming back *immediately after* the tribulation. Also please notice verse 31. When He comes, He is coming back 'with a great *sound of a trumpet*,' and '*will gather together His elect at that time.*'"

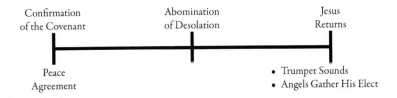

Confirmation of the Covenant — Abomination of Desolation — Jesus Returns

Peace Agreement

- Trumpet Sounds
- Angels Gather His Elect

"Matthew," Oliver continued, "some people in this room believe the 'elect' refers to the Jews. Some understand the 'elect' to be Christians, and some, I'm sure, do not know or have never thought about it. Matthew, who are the elect?"

"Well, Mr. Stuart, since you told me yesterday that you would be asking me this question, I have been talking to Paul about this and reading his letters on this fancy thing you call an iPad. I will tell you what I've learned.

"If you look at the opening of Paul's letter to the Romans, he is addressing 'those who are called to belong to Jesus Christ' in verse 6, and in verse 7, 'To all those in Rome who are loved by God and called to be saints.' This tells me that Paul is writing to believers, or as you call them, Christians.

"Then, later in his letter, Romans 11:7, Paul says Israel failed to obtain something, and the elect, or election, did obtain it. This tells me that Israel, or the Jewish people, and the 'elect' cannot be the same thing. If one obtained something and the other did not, they can't be the same."

"Thank you, Matthew." Oliver walked over to address the jury. "Ladies and gentlemen, I have Exhibit 14 up on the screen and in your binders. I will read it aloud in two different translations."

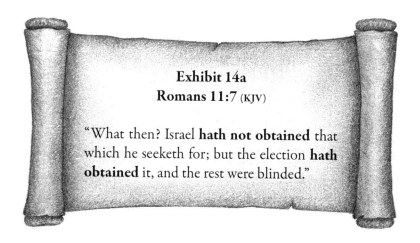

Exhibit 14a
Romans 11:7 (KJV)

"What then? Israel **hath not obtained** that which he seeketh for; but the election **hath obtained** it, and the rest were blinded."

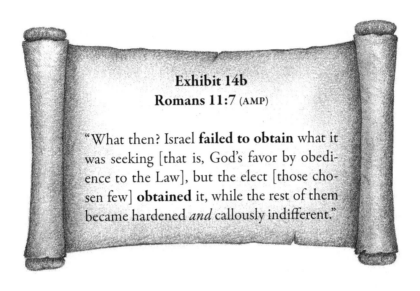

Exhibit 14b
Romans 11:7 (AMP)

"What then? Israel **failed to obtain** what it was seeking [that is, God's favor by obedience to the Law], but the elect [those chosen few] **obtained** it, while the rest of them became hardened *and* callously indifferent."

"This verse, ladies and gentlemen, describes the elect as those who obtained something that Israel, or the Jews, did not. Therefore, 'the elect' in this verse cannot refer to the Jewish people. Matthew, do you have any other comments about the identity of the elect?"

"Yes, Mr. Stuart. I do have one more example for you. If you read verse 2 at the opening of Paul's letter to the Colossians, he tells you exactly who he is speaking to. He is speaking directly to the church, 'To the saints and faithful brothers in Christ.' Then, in 3:12, he identifies them as 'the elect of God.' There is no doubt, then, as to the identity of 'the elect.'"

"Thank you, Matthew. Ladies and gentlemen, please refer to Exhibits 15 and 16 in your binders, as I read them aloud."

Exhibit 15
Colossians 1:1-2 (ESV)

"¹Paul, an apostle of Christ Jesus by the will of God, and Timothy our brother,
²To the saints and faithful brothers in Christ at Colossae: Grace to you and peace from God our Father."

Exhibit 16
Colossians 3:12-13 (KJV)

"¹²Put on therefore, as the **elect of God**, holy and beloved, bowels of mercies, kindness, humbleness of mind, meekness, longsuffering;
¹³Forbearing one another, and forgiving one another, if any man have a quarrel against any: even as Christ forgave you, so also do ye."

"Ladies and gentlemen," Oliver continued, "from these two

examples, we can conclude that 'the elect' are believers in Jesus, and Matthew just read for us Exhibit 13, in which Jesus himself said He is coming back immediately after the tribulation and will gather His elect at that time."

Chapter 15

What Event Will Start the Great Tribulation?

O liver proceeded: "Matthew, many people in our town believe the Great Tribulation will last for seven years. However, Jesus told you that this period of great tribulation will begin in the middle of the final seven years."

"Actually, what He said was that when we see the Abomination of Desolation that Daniel talked about, then there will be great tribulation, and we know from Daniel that the Abomination of Desolation happens in the middle of the final seven-year period."

"So what you are really saying, Matthew, is that if Jesus said the Abomination of Desolation starts the Great Tribulation, which happens in the middle of the seven years, then what we really have is a three-and-a-half-year tribulation period, not a seven-year tribulation period?"

"That is correct."

"Ladies and gentlemen of the jury, please refer at this time to Exhibit 17, Matthew 24:15-21, in which Matthew is quoting Jesus Christ. Please pay special attention to verses 15 and 21. In verse 15, Jesus refers to the Abomination of Desolation that Daniel talked about. In verse 21, Jesus explains that when you see the Abomination of Desolation, this event will begin a period of great tribulation worse than has ever been since the beginning of the world or will ever be.

"Matthew, will you please read your writing aloud for the court at this time, Exhibit 17."

"Certainly." Matthew began reading from the iPad in Greek:

Ὅταν οὖν ἴδητε τὸ βδέλυγμα τῆς ἐρημώσεως τὸ ῥηθὲν διὰ Δανιὴλ τοῦ προφήτου ἑστὸς ἐν τόπῳ ἁγίῳ, ὁ ἀναγινώσκων νοείτω, τότε οἱ ἐν τῇ Ἰουδαίᾳ φευγέτωσαν εἰς τὰ ὄρη, ὁ ἐπὶ τοῦ δώματος μὴ καταβάτω ἆραι τὰ ἐκ τῆς οἰκίας αὐτοῦ, καὶ ὁ ἐν τῷ ἀγρῷ μὴ ἐπιστρεψάτω ὀπίσω ἆραι τὸ ἱμάτιον αὐτοῦ. Οὐαὶ δὲ ταῖς ἐν γαστρὶ ἐχούσαις καὶ ταῖς θηλαζούσαις ἐν ἐκείναις ταῖς ἡμέραις. Προσεύχεσθε δὲ ἵνα μὴ γένηται ἡ φυγὴ ὑμῶν χειμῶνος μηδὲ σαββάτῳ. Ἔσται γὰρ τότε θλῖψις μεγάλη οἵα οὐ γέγονεν ἀπ' ἀρχῆς κόσμου ἕως τοῦ νῦν οὐδ' οὐ μὴ γένηται.

Oliver directed everyone to the screen and to their exhibit binders to read the passage in the King James Version and compare it to the Amplified Version.

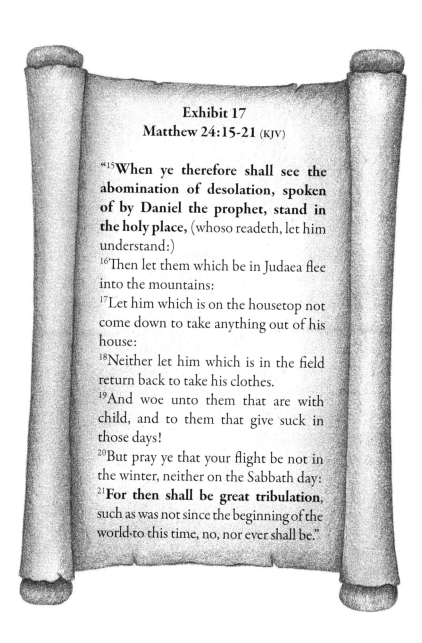

Exhibit 17
Matthew 24:15-21 (KJV)

"¹⁵**When ye therefore shall see the abomination of desolation, spoken of by Daniel the prophet, stand in the holy place,** (whoso readeth, let him understand:)

¹⁶Then let them which be in Judaea flee into the mountains:

¹⁷Let him which is on the housetop not come down to take anything out of his house:

¹⁸Neither let him which is in the field return back to take his clothes.

¹⁹And woe unto them that are with child, and to them that give suck in those days!

²⁰But pray ye that your flight be not in the winter, neither on the Sabbath day:

²¹**For then shall be great tribulation,** such as was not since the beginning of the world to this time, no, nor ever shall be."

Exhibit 18
Matthew 24:15-21 (AMP)

"15So when you see the abomination of desolation [the appalling sacrilege that astonishes and makes desolate], spoken of by the prophet Daniel, standing in the Holy Place (let the reader understand), 16then let those who are in Judea flee to the mountains [for refuge]. 17Whoever is on the housetop must not go down to get the things that are in his house [because there will not be enough time]. 18Whoever is in the field must not turn back to get his coat. 19And woe to those who are pregnant and to those who are nursing babies in those days! 20Pray that your flight [from persecution and suffering] will not be in winter, or on a Sabbath [when Jewish laws prohibit travel]. 21For at that time there will be a great tribulation such as has not occurred since the beginning of the world until now, nor ever will [(pressure, distress, oppression), again]."

"Thank you, Matthew. And thank you for being one of our special guests today. Your Honor, I have no more questions for this witness."

"Thank you, counselor. You may step down, Matthew. Please continue, Mr. Stuart."

"Ladies and gentlemen, we have absolute proof that according to Jesus Christ himself, the event known as the Abomination of Desolation, which starts *in the middle* of the final seven years, will start the Great Tribulation.

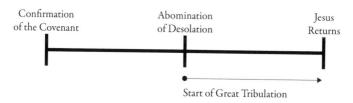

"This brings us to a dilemma," Oliver said. "Many people in our town are of the understanding that tribulation will continue for seven years. If Jesus said it will begin in the middle of the seven years, then we must conclude that the period known as the Great Tribulation is only going to be a three-and-a-half-year period."

Chapter 16

How Long Will the Great Tribulation Last?

O liver continued his argument: "Ladies and gentlemen of the jury, in addition to the words of Jesus Christ himself describing a three-and-a-half-year tribulation period, there are six more verses in the Bible that describe a three-and-a-half-year period. I would like to draw your attention to these verses at this time. They are printed in your exhibit binders as Exhibit 19, and I have them here on the screen for everyone to see. They are written by two people we have already had on the witness stand: the prophet Daniel and the apostle John.

"And just for the record, there are no verses that describe a seven-year tribulation period. There *is* a seven-year period, but as we have examined, great tribulation happens during the second half.

"Again, please refer to your exhibit binders as I explain," Oliver said. "If we cross-reference the content of Daniel 7:25 with that of Revelation 13:5, we can conclude that a time equals one year, times equals two years, and the dividing of time equals half a year; totaling three-and-a-half years or forty-two months. We can tell from the context that these two verses are speaking of the same three-and-a-half-year period. Daniel refers to it as 'a time, and times, and the dividing of time.' John refers to it as forty-two months. I will read Exhibits 20 and 21 aloud while you follow along in your binders."

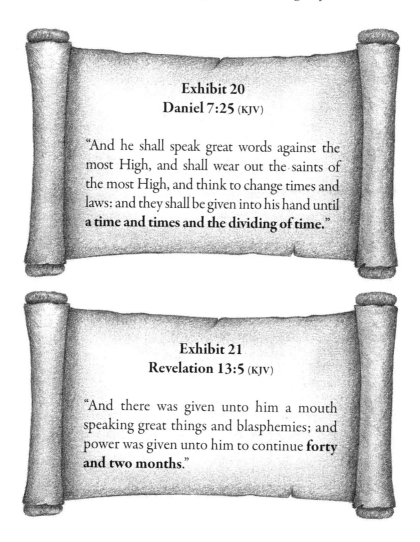

Exhibit 20
Daniel 7:25 (KJV)

"And he shall speak great words against the most High, and shall wear out the saints of the most High, and think to change times and laws: and they shall be given into his hand until **a time and times and the dividing of time.**"

Exhibit 21
Revelation 13:5 (KJV)

"And there was given unto him a mouth speaking great things and blasphemies; and power was given unto him to continue **forty and two months.**"

Oliver continued, "We can conclude from Daniel and John, ladies and gentlemen, that this is the same three-and-a-half-year time period in which the Antichrist will rule. Now we will examine the other four passages, and please notice the descriptions as we read: forty-two months, a time, and times, and half a time, and the specific number of days.

"Please see Exhibit 22. Also, note for the record that we have read this same scripture passage earlier in our proceedings."

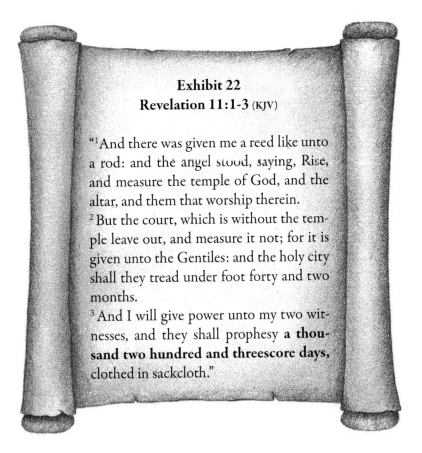

Exhibit 22
Revelation 11:1-3 (KJV)

"¹And there was given me a reed like unto a rod: and the angel stood, saying, Rise, and measure the temple of God, and the altar, and them that worship therein.
² But the court, which is without the temple leave out, and measure it not; for it is given unto the Gentiles: and the holy city shall they tread under foot forty and two months.
³ And I will give power unto my two witnesses, and they shall prophesy **a thousand two hundred and threescore days,** clothed in sackcloth."

"Ladies and gentlemen," Oliver said, "the King James translation uses the term 'threescore days.' The New International Version translates 'threescore days' as 60 days, giving us 1,260 days, which is seventeen-and-a-half days short of three-and-a-half years in our western calendar. Exactly three-and-a-half years in the Hebrew calendar. Please also notice that in the verse we just read, Revelation 11:3, we see God's Two Witnesses at work during the same 1,260 days. So, at the same time the Antichrist is reigning, the Two Witnesses will be at work."

Oliver advanced the PowerPoint to the next slide. "Let's continue to the next verse. See Exhibit 23, Daniel 12:11."

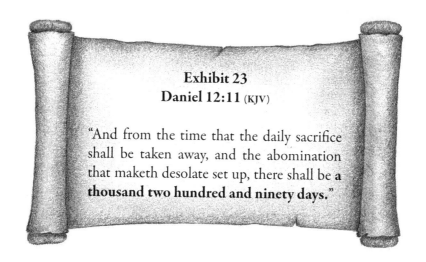

Exhibit 23
Daniel 12:11 (KJV)

"And from the time that the daily sacrifice shall be taken away, and the abomination that maketh desolate set up, there shall be **a thousand two hundred and ninety days.**"

He read it aloud.

"1,290 days is twelve-and-a-half days longer than three-and-a-half years. And here is one more verse: Exhibit 24, Revelation 12:14."

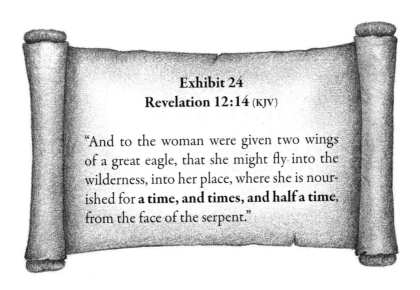

Exhibit 24
Revelation 12:14 (KJV)

"And to the woman were given two wings of a great eagle, that she might fly into the wilderness, into her place, where she is nourished for **a time, and times, and half a time,** from the face of the serpent."

"So, ladies and gentlemen," Oliver said, "you can see we have ample proof that the Great Tribulation will last for a time period of three-and-a-half years."

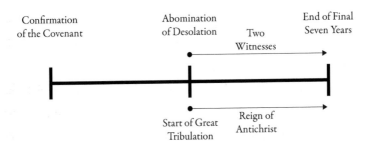

Judge Kane raised his gavel and announced, "The hour is getting late. Court is in recess. We will reconvene again tomorrow morning at 9:00 a.m."

That night, Holly decided to sneak out to the homestead and spy on her brother and sister-in-law and those guys he hired, which she assumed were staying with them. Holly told her husband and her folks that she was heading over to Oliver's.

It was a nice evening and still light out as she approached the homestead around 8:00 p.m. Fortunately, Oliver and Amy had a long driveway with trees on either side. They also had a row of big pine trees along the road, providing even more privacy. Holly parked by the pine trees and walked the rest of the way so that no one would see her. The cornstalks on the neighbor's property were just the right height and provided a perfect place for her to hide.

They were all sitting outside around a campfire. It looked like they were making s'mores, and Holly could hear them talking in foreign languages. She put in her translation device to see if she could understand the conversation. Oliver and Amy were there with Daniel, John, and Matthew, along with Ben and two of his friends that had been with them all week. She didn't see Paul, and she could barely make out the conversation because of the distance.

Daniel, speaking to John and Matthew, said, "It's remarkable hearing all about the time you spent with our Messiah, Jesus. Equally wonderful getting to know you both, and Paul too, in this future time."

Holly was so confused. "It sounds as though these people are not actors, but it makes no sense for them to be who they say they are," she thought. "Why on earth would they speak this way if it were not so?"

Just then, the screen door slammed, and Paul came out of the house along with the family dog, who had become affectionately attached to Paul and followed him wherever he went while at the homestead. Holly had forgotten about Max, their new dog that she had not yet met. Pretty soon, the German Shepherd started barking and running over to the cornstalks where Holly was hiding. She realized that she was caught, so she came out.

Oliver announced, "Hey, Holly is here. What are you doing in the cornstalks? Where is your car? Are you spying on us?"

Amy welcomed her. "Hi, Holly! So glad you came out tonight."

"Thanks, Amy. I really want to know who these people are and what's really going on."

"I know you do, and we want you to know too. Have you met Ben before?"

"Yes, I met him years ago when Ollie was in college and then again at your wedding."

"Oh, that's right, Ben was Ollie's best man. Well, as you might know, Ben is kind of a risk-taker, and it was his idea to bring Paul, John, Daniel, and Matthew here for our town trial."

"Bring them here?" Holly questioned. "What are you talking about? That isn't even possible."

Amy explained, "Holly, I'm going to tell you some highly classified information that will likely become worldwide news very soon. Ben and I, along with several others, recently returned from two top-secret government assignments involving a time machine. Ben was chosen to be the test pilot, and our team successfully traveled back in time and returned home safe. When our missions were complete, it was Ben's idea to "borrow" the time machine and go back in time to find Paul and the others for Oliver's court case."

"Did you say 'missions,' as in more than one? Do you have proof? Pictures? Video?"

"Yes, we went on two official missions, and yes, we do have proof. In fact, a little bit later, we can go inside and share pictures and videos with you. Right now, though, let me have the honor and privilege of introducing you to the apostles Paul, John, and Matthew and to the prophet Daniel."

Holly got all choked up. Barely able to speak, the tears began running down her face. She was overflowing with gratefulness and the utmost respect for these men. She was full of joy for this opportunity and thankful for their example and obedience to God.

"Guys," Amy said, "I would like to introduce you to Holly, Oliver's sister."

They all stood up to greet her. "Very nice to meet you, Holly. Happy you came to our campfire tonight." She wasn't quite sure what to do next, so she gave each of them a big hug.

Oliver was so excited! He had wanted Holly to know the whole time that they were not just actors.

Holly asked, "Do Mom and Dad know?"

"Not yet," Oliver answered.

"Can we tell them? I'll call them right now. They can drive over and bring Nate and the boys."

"Well, I would like them to know too, of course. I'm just worried about the media getting wind of this."

Holly responded, "Don't worry, Ollie, this will all work out. Nobody believes in time travel." She pulled out her phone and called her husband, Nate.

Soon, Nate and their two boys, ages fourteen and seventeen, arrived with Grandma and Grandpa. At Holly's request, Nate collected the boys' cell phones before introductions. She didn't want them texting or posting any pictures online. Equally important, she wanted their full attention during the evening.

Oliver made sure everyone had a translation device, and they sat by the campfire, getting to know one another, listening to stories, and later on—looking at pictures and video from the time travel trips.

It was an incredible evening, not just for the Norton family and for Holly and Oliver's parents, but also for Daniel, Paul, Matthew, and John. They, too, got to see videos of creation and Noah's Ark. It was just as Moses had described it, they thought. When it was time to leave, Holly's oldest son, Nick, asked permission to stay overnight with his aunt and uncle at the homestead.

"That will be fine," Amy said. "He can ride into town with Oliver in the morning before court begins."

Chapter 17

Will Christians Be on the Earth During the Final Three-and-a-Half Years?

O n Friday morning, Holly ate breakfast at the local diner with her friend Lucy before the morning session. Lucy was not too concerned with the timing of the rapture. She liked going to church to see her friends, to worship the Lord, to sing, and to hear what the pastor had to say each week. She didn't see why there was such a big debate over the timing of the rapture or how it had any relevance to her life. Her personal relationship with God and sharing Christ with others were much more important to her than debating about when Jesus is going to rapture the church. However, the court hearings spurred some interest in the prophesied end-time events. Lucy had friends on both sides of the debate, so she was trying to understand each view and maintain her friendships.

"Holly, in your opinion, when a person gets saved, is the Holy Spirit involved?" Lucy asked.

"Yes, of course, Lucy, you know that. Why are you asking?"

"Well, I got to thinking about something you said during your speech to the jury. You said the Holy Spirit is taken away from the earth when the church is raptured . . . at the beginning of the seven years. I think you called the Holy Spirit the restrainer. Is that right?"

"Yes, that's what I said. Why do you ask?"

"Well, because I know there are verses that say there will be Christians on the earth during the Great Tribulation. So, if all the Christians disappear right before the final seven years, then how can anyone become a Christian during the Great Tribulation if the Holy Spirit has left the earth? You said you agree with me that no one can become a Christian without the Holy Spirit being involved. So, I guess I was just thinking about that. Also, the Two Witnesses that Oliver talked about must be filled with the Holy Spirit to fulfill their mission."

"Those are good points," said Holly. She looked at her watch, and when she realized what time it was, she said, "We better get to court, or we are going to be late. Let's continue our conversation later."

They arrived just as Oliver began speaking. "Your Honor and members of the jury, today I will prove to you that Christians will still be on the earth during the final seven years, which, of course, includes the final three-and-a-half years, or the Great Tribulation period." He looked down at his notes and addressed the courtroom. "I would like to begin with Daniel 7:25 and focus on the 'he.'"

"Very well, counselor. However, I don't see your witnesses with you this morning. Are they running late?"

"No, Your Honor." Oliver pauses. "Actually, um, well . . . they are missing."

"Missing?"

"Yes, Your Honor. I'm so sorry. My car is missing too, so I'm sure they just went for a ride. They must have gotten lost. I'm sure Ben will find them soon and bring them back to court."

"Mr. Stuart, if you don't have any witnesses to bring to the stand, that will be a problem."

"Yes, of course, I see your point, Your Honor. You are correct. I would not be allowed to continue making my case without any witnesses in a real courtroom trial. Would you like to suspend the proceedings until the men come back?"

There was quiet whispering and anticipation among the people in the courtroom. It was obvious the people wanted to hear Oliver's thoughts even though he would be breaking the rules. Judge Kane contemplated. People murmured and waited anxiously.

"Ladies and gentlemen," Judge Kane declared, "this is highly unusual, but so is everything else with this trial, so for a short time, I will allow Mr. Stuart to continue presenting his case using Scripture, even though the witnesses are not present. In addition, Mr. Stuart, when making your case, I will ask you to state that this is your opinion versus fact."

"Yes, of course, Your Honor. Thank you for allowing me to proceed. It is my opinion that the 'he' in Daniel 7:25 refers to the Antichrist. 'He' will wear out the saints of the Most High for three-and-a-half years. So, yes, in my opinion, Christians will be here during the final three-and-a-half years.

"I will read aloud Exhibit 25, Daniel 7:25, noting that I have read this verse before." Oliver turned to the screen.

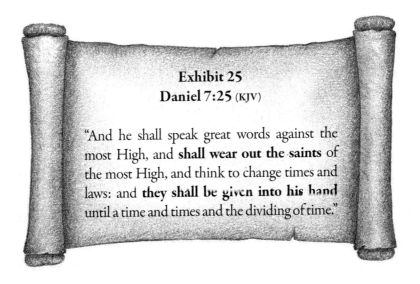

Exhibit 25
Daniel 7:25 (KJV)

"And he shall speak great words against the most High, and **shall wear out the saints** of the most High, and think to change times and laws: and **they shall be given into his hand** until a time and times and the dividing of time."

He continued: "You will also see, ladies and gentlemen, that in Revelation 13:7, John records that the Antichrist will make war with the saints and overcome them—which, in my opinion, gives us further confirmation that Christians will still be here on earth during the final three-and-a-half years." Oliver turned the page in his binder.

"I have Exhibit 26 up on the screen, as well as in your binders." He read from the screen.

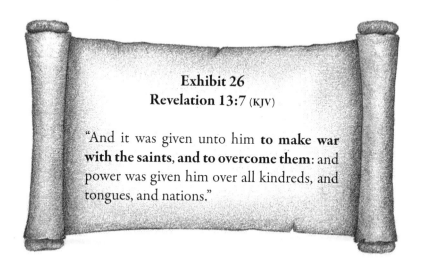

Exhibit 26
Revelation 13:7 (KJV)

"And it was given unto him **to make war with the saints, and to overcome them:** and power was given him over all kindreds, and tongues, and nations."

"In addition, ladies and gentlemen, in my opinion, during the three-and-a-half-year reign of the Antichrist, Christians and Jews will be under attack if they are living in areas of the world where the Antichrist has taken control. Christians will not worship the Antichrist, or his image, or receive his mark on their foreheads or their hands.[1]

"We find a third confirmation that Christians will be on the earth during the Great Tribulation in Revelation 20:4, in which some Christians will be beheaded for their witness of Jesus. I will read for you Exhibit 27."

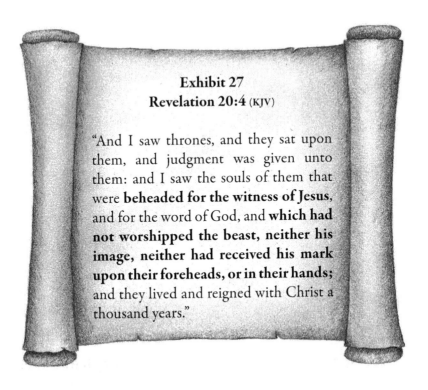

Exhibit 27
Revelation 20:4 (KJV)

"And I saw thrones, and they sat upon them, and judgment was given unto them: and I saw the souls of them that were **beheaded for the witness of Jesus,** and for the word of God, and **which had not worshipped the beast, neither his image, neither had received his mark upon their foreheads, or in their hands;** and they lived and reigned with Christ a thousand years."

"In my opinion, these verses tell us that Christians have not been raptured yet and will still be here during the reign of the Antichrist."

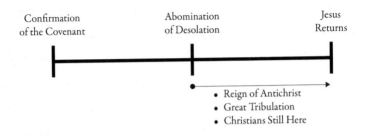

| Confirmation of the Covenant | Abomination of Desolation | Jesus Returns |

- Reign of Antichrist
- Great Tribulation
- Christians Still Here

Chapter 18

Bringing the Saints with Him

"**C**ontinuing on, Your Honor," Oliver said, "I will present evidence from the prophet Zechariah from the Old Testament."

Judge Kane replied, "Are you also going to bring the prophet Zechariah here in person?"

"No, Your Honor. Zechariah is not here with us today. I will need to continue presenting my case with only the words from the Bible."

"Very well, proceed with the same stipulation that everyone here is aware that you are giving your opinion versus facts."

"Yes, Your Honor. Thank you. Zechariah wrote that when the Lord returns to earth at the Battle of Armageddon, He is bringing the saints with Him,[1] implying that the rapture of the church has already occurred. I agree with Zechariah. However, we saw in Exhibit 13, Matthew 24:29-31, that Jesus told Matthew and the other disciples that when He comes, *immediately after* the tribulation, He is going to gather His elect at that time, referring to Christians. I know this appears to be somewhat of a contradiction. Let's see if I can shed some light on this.

"I would like to propose to the jury that when Jesus is coming down at the second coming, Christians are going up in the rapture. According to Paul, they meet in the air. We have already been over Paul's exact description of this in 1 Thessalonians 4:17, which I have up on the screen. I am emphasizing the words 'to meet the Lord in the air.'" He gestured to the quote on the screen.

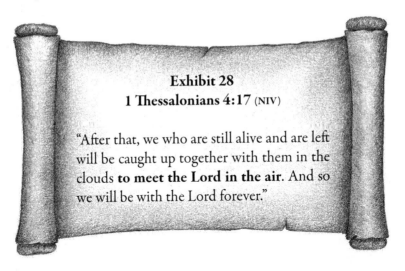

Exhibit 28
1 Thessalonians 4:17 (NIV)

"After that, we who are still alive and are left will be caught up together with them in the clouds **to meet the Lord in the air**. And so we will be with the Lord forever."

"The words 'to meet the Lord in the air' tell us that those who are 'caught up' or raptured, will be meeting the Lord in the air as 'they shall see the Son of Man coming in the clouds of heaven' (Matthew 24:30). I added that last part from Matthew's gospel account." Oliver advanced to the next image on the screen.

Exhibit 29
Matthew 24:30 (NIV)

"Then will appear the sign of the Son of Man in heaven. And then all the peoples of the earth will mourn when they see the Son of Man coming on the clouds of heaven, with power and great glory."

"Now," Oliver said, "let's look at Exhibit 30, Zechariah's account in which all the saints will come with Christ when He returns."

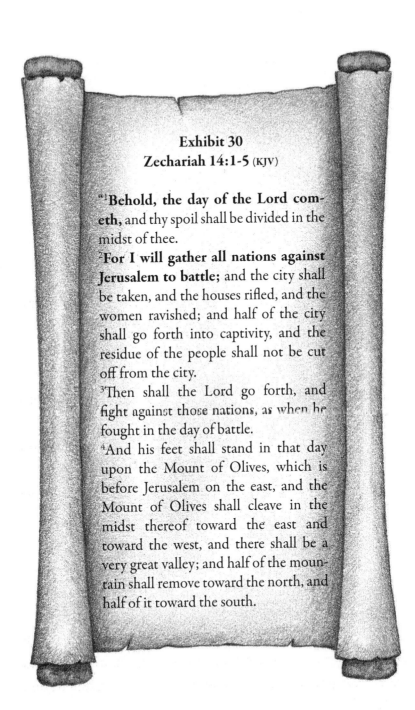

Exhibit 30
Zechariah 14:1-5 (KJV)

"¹Behold, the day of the Lord cometh, and thy spoil shall be divided in the midst of thee.
²For I will gather all nations against Jerusalem to battle; and the city shall be taken, and the houses rifled, and the women ravished; and half of the city shall go forth into captivity, and the residue of the people shall not be cut off from the city.
³Then shall the Lord go forth, and fight against those nations, as when he fought in the day of battle.
⁴And his feet shall stand in that day upon the Mount of Olives, which is before Jerusalem on the east, and the Mount of Olives shall cleave in the midst thereof toward the east and toward the west, and there shall be a very great valley; and half of the mountain shall remove toward the north, and half of it toward the south.

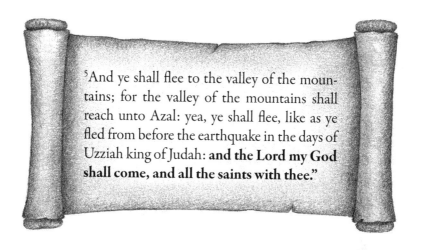

> [5]And ye shall flee to the valley of the mountains; for the valley of the mountains shall reach unto Azal: yea, ye shall flee, like as ye fled from before the earthquake in the days of Uzziah king of Judah: **and the Lord my God shall come, and all the saints with thee."**

Oliver directed everyone's attention to the screen with a summary of Zechariah's description of the second coming during the Battle of Armageddon.

1. *The Lord will gather all nations against Jerusalem to battle (verse 2).*
2. *The Lord will go out and fight against those nations (verse 3).*
3. *His feet shall stand on the Mount of Olives that lies before Jerusalem (verse 4).*
4. *The Mount of Olives will be split in two (verse 4).*
5. *The Lord will come, 'and all the holy ones with Him' (verse 5, ESV).*

"Again," he said, "I propose that immediately *after* the tribulation, Exhibit 13, born-again Christians[2] will meet Jesus in the air, Exhibit 28, and will then go with Him to the Mount of Olives as it says in Zechariah 14. The Lord will come, 'and all the holy ones with Him,' Exhibit 30. The rapture and the second coming, then, in my opinion, are the same event."

The townspeople in the courtroom were quite surprised at Oliver's confident assertion that these two momentous end-time events occur simultaneously. There was a sudden rise of murmuring throughout the courtroom.

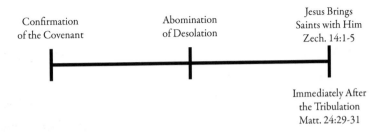

Judge Kane struck his gavel on the hardwood sound block and declared, "Court is in recess. We will break and reconvene at 1:30 p.m."

During the break, Ben showed up and told Oliver and Amy that he couldn't find Nick or the guys. They could be anywhere.

They couldn't call Nick because they had confiscated his cell phone the night before at the campfire.

Unbeknownst to Ben, Oliver, and Amy, here is what happened. Paul, John, Matthew and Daniel woke up very early and decided to wake up Nick. They convinced him to take them out for a ride in Oliver's old red Cadillac convertible. Nick was reluctant at first, but he found the keys and figured they would be back in time for breakfast.

He drove them out in the middle of nowhere so that they could take turns learning how to drive. The men had great fun, and Nick lost track of the time. It was hard for him to believe where he was and who he was with. After a while, they weren't quite sure where they were. Eventually, Nick spotted the Cherry Creek water tower and drove towards it until he recognized his surroundings again. He wanted to drive directly to the courthouse, but the guys talked him into doing some sightseeing. This adventure was way more fun than hanging out at Grandma and Grandpa's place.

Soon, they were walking down Main Street, going in and out of stores, and looking at all there was to see. As lunchtime approached, they were hungry, especially since they had skipped breakfast. The aroma of food drew them into a little restaurant. Nick ordered pizza and root beer for everyone.

Ben, Amy, Oliver, and Holly tried to figure out what to do next. "Where could they be?" said Oliver, exasperated.

"I looked everywhere," said Ben.

Just then, someone shouted at Oliver, "Hey, Stuart, it looks like your car is parked over on Main Street. Guess your guys didn't skip town after all."

They jumped in Amy's car and went to find the red Cadillac. Soon, they found Nick and the men eating pizza and were greatly relieved. They ordered extra food and enjoyed lunch together.

At 1:00 p.m., Ben and Amy started receiving texts from their time travel friends and the base team. The news about the time machine would break at 3:00 p.m. Central Standard Time. It was going to be a momentous event. Both live and pre-recorded interviews were scheduled to broadcast, and people all over the world would see footage of Noah's Ark, the animals, dinosaurs, and people living during that time. They would see video from the third day of creation of trees sprouting up from the ground, growing to full size within minutes. For obvious reasons, the location of the secret base for the time machine would not be released.

Ben did some quick thinking and made a few calls. He wanted to get himself and the men to a more private location—away from news reporters. First, he called a retired military buddy who owned and operated a helicopter charter company. Ben had been wanting to get these guys in a chopper during their visit, and this was his chance. Fortunately, his friend was available and agreed to help him. They arranged to meet at the Stuart homestead at 3:00 p.m. Next, Ben called another friend who had a cabin on an island on Lake Minnetonka. Ben's friend agreed to host the men on the island for the weekend and to keep their identities secret—except from the people helping to host them. So far, no one in the media knew anything about Matthew, John, Paul, and Daniel being brought from the past. The island would provide them safety from the media and some enjoyment on the lake.

Chapter 19

The Lord Will Come Like a Thief in the Night

At one-thirty on Friday afternoon, court resumed for the final session of the week. Oliver began. "Your Honor, members of the court, Daniel, Paul, Matthew, and John are all here with us now."

Judge Kane looked a little surprised to see the men. He had assumed the actors had stolen the car and skipped town. "You may proceed with your witnesses, Mr. Stuart."

"Thank you, Your Honor. I call again to the stand the apostle Paul."

Once Paul had taken the stand, Oliver said, "Paul, thank you again for being here with us today. Paul, many people in our town believe that when Jesus returns, it will be a surprise and we will not know when He is coming. In fact, many people quote you saying, 'the Lord will come like a thief in the night,' believing this means that the rapture will be a surprise and no one will know the timing. However, you say we will not be surprised because we are children of light, children of the day."

"Yes. That is correct. Those who are not in darkness will not be surprised. I wrote to the church in Thessalonica: '**For you yourselves are fully aware that the day of the Lord will come like a thief in the night.** While people are saying, "There is peace and security," then sudden destruction will come upon them as labor pains come upon a pregnant woman, and they will not escape. **But you are not in darkness, brothers, for that day to surprise you like a thief. For you are all children of light, children of the day.** We are not of the night or of the darkness.' "[1]

"So, what you are actually saying, Paul, is that if we are children of light, we will not be surprised."

"That is correct."

"Thank you again, Paul. Your Honor, I have no further questions for this witness at this time."

Judge Kane dismissed Paul from the stand, and he returned to his seat.

Oliver continued, "Once again, ladies and gentlemen, God has used the writers of the Bible to let us know that if we are paying attention to the prophecies, we will be able to follow the sequence of events playing out on the world scene. This allows us to prepare ourselves, and especially to help others prepare, for eternal salvation.

"Your Honor," Oliver said, "at this time, I would like to make a motion for a continuance." Before he could finish with an explanation, the judge agreed. It was Friday and it was hot, and many people in Minnesota leave work early on Fridays in the summer. The judge was ready for the weekend.

"Very well, court is now in recess. We will reconvene on Monday at 9:00 a.m."

Amy, Ben, and Oliver rushed the men back to the homestead and told them the news that was about to hit the world. They also prepared them for the helicopter that was about to pick them up. Ben would go with them to the island. Amy dug through some drawers, looking for swimsuits or shorts the men could wear at the lake. Oliver talked them into changing into some of his casual clothes and shoes. They quickly packed food and extra translation devices, and then the men watched as the helicopter approached. They couldn't believe their eyes. Never could they have imagined something such as this. John, however, got goosebumps. There was something vaguely familiar to him about this. It was almost as if he had seen something similar in one of his visions.[2]

Oliver told Ben that he only needed the men for one more day in court. He expected the trial to be complete by the end of the day on Monday. Ben promised to get them back by Monday morning.

Over the weekend, no one in the small town could stop talking about the case. Most of them had agreed with Holly and her slam-dunk case for a pre-tribulation rapture. Children and teenagers were now asking their parents about the Bible. Dinner conversations revolved around the people who God chose to write the Bible.

The news story about the time machine broke Friday afternoon, and the two official time travel trips became top stories all over the world. People in Cherry Creek began to wonder about the witnesses in court. What if the people pretending to be from the Bible were not actors? What if they were who they said they were and had somehow traveled here in the time machine? This would explain the foreign languages, the translation devices, the clothes, and the odd questions asked by the witnesses. They wondered if perhaps they had been watching the real Paul, John, Daniel, and Matthew.

Amy, Oliver, and Holly, along with their parents, spent most of Friday evening going from house to house asking as many people as possible to please keep the town trial and the Bible guests a secret, at least until after the men left on Monday. They explained that the men were out of town for the weekend but would return for one more day to finish the trial before being returned to their own time. They weren't sure if the secret would be kept or not, but the townspeople did feel privileged that these guests had come to their town and that they would get to see them one more time on Monday.

On Sunday morning, the churches in town were full of people. They came earlier and they stayed much later after the service to discuss and read the Bible. Some were confused because Oliver seemed to be using several of the same scriptures that Holly had used. Now, however, some of the townspeople had doubts and were starting to wonder if they would be here on earth until the end of the final seven years. The prospect was sobering, and they began to take more of an interest in the prophecies that Oliver had been trying to tell them about in their community Bible study.

Chapter 20

The Island

Big Island. Lake Minnetonka,
Minnesota. Friday evening.

The time travelers thoroughly enjoyed their flight to the island. They were in the air for about an hour. Ben wanted them to see the cities, the farms, the Minneapolis airport, the freeways, the skyscrapers, and much more from the air. They flew over Lake Minnetonka and saw big boats, fast boats, and fancy sailboats with colorful sails. They flew over large homes and estates on the mainland, then over to the island. There was a small clearing up on a hill where the helicopter landed. The pilot agreed to pick them back up early Monday morning and to keep this trip and its passengers quiet at Ben's request.

Ben introduced Paul, Daniel, John, and Matthew to his friend, Mandi, who was a descendant of the Scriver family. The Scriver family came to the island in 1900, and their descendants occupied four cabins near Crown Point. Mandi's second and third cousins were wonderful hosts over the weekend and promised to conceal their guests' real identities and to refrain from sharing any photos until after they left the island. Ben asked the men not to tell anyone about the court case or that they had been in a place called Cherry Creek. They simply divulged that they had come here in the now-known time machine and for reasons they were not going to explain, they needed a place to hide for the weekend.

Upon their arrival, they got a tour and enjoyed meeting family members. Ben distributed translation devices so that everyone could understand each other. The island was an ideal place to hide from the general public and the media. The time machine was now global news. But almost no one yet knew it had been used to bring people from the past to the present.

The island was a peaceful place with beautiful trees and stunning views of the big lake. It was quite different from the small town. In one cabin, there was a jigsaw puzzle on the table that was halfway completed. Daniel found this interesting, and he hoped that he would have time to help fit the pieces together.

The big green cabin had a screened-in porch with old sails and dock rope decorating the ceiling. The family collected sunglasses when they snorkeled and hung them on string from the ceiling, kind of like a miniature clothesline. Cabin guests were often offered a pair of sunglasses to keep. Each of the men tried on different pairs and kept one for themselves. "What a great invention," they thought.

After visiting a while on the porch, they walked down a hill on a dirt path through the trees where more cabins lined the shore. The men were comfortable around water, and John asked if they could go fishing in the morning.

Ben said, "I don't think we can go fishing. We don't have fishing licenses."

"Fishing licenses?" John replied.

"Yeah, we need permission to fish."

"Wow, strange! So, let's get fishing licenses."

"Well," said Ben, "That's complicated. You need an identification card, which you don't have. And no one would believe your date of birth. I don't want to draw attention to you."

"I agree," John said. I will pray and ask God if we can fish tomorrow."

Although there were no cars on the island, they did see many types of boats and even a golf cart for transporting supplies up and down the hill.

Paul inquired about the sailboats and saw that the wind was good for a sail. After dinner, the island hosts were happy to take the men sailing. Paul took a turn at the helm and told of his adventures on much larger ships that carried well over two hundred people.[1] The island hosts were captivated by the stories of his dangerous journeys spreading the gospel, including the three times he was shipwrecked and the one time he was adrift at sea for a night and a day.[2]

That evening, Ben learned that the State of Minnesota had launched a campaign to boost enthusiasm for fishing. Anyone could fish without a license on Saturdays in July. John was pleased and thankful to God for answering his prayer.

Saturday morning, the lake was like glass. The hosts showed John and Daniel how to fish off the dock with fishing poles. John found the process slow and inefficient. "Can we go out in a boat?" he asked, adding, "Where are your nets?"

The island hosts explained that they didn't do a lot of fishing and that they had never used big nets. "Fishing is more of a pastime than a necessity."

"Really?" John said.

After some time on the pontoon, they had caught a dozen sunnies and crappies, enough for lunch, fried in the firepit by the lake.

While John and Daniel fished from the pontoon, Paul and Matthew rode along in a boat pulling a water skier. They enjoyed the speed! Balanced on a single ski, the skier created giant walls of spraying water. Matthew shouted over the motor, "It would be marvelous to have a boat like this on the Sea of Galilee!"

Daniel made sure that Ben brought along the iPad on the trip. He had quickly become addicted to reading the New Testament and saturating himself with the knowledge of Jesus's life. Ben had packed enough iPads for each of the men to read in their own language. On Saturday afternoon, the men rested from all the activity and water adventures and spent time in solitude. They soaked up God's Word like a sponge. The island hosts gained a renewed interest in reading their own Bibles. If they didn't have theirs with them, they downloaded Bible apps.

In the evenings, everyone sat around the campfire by the lake, asking questions and listening to first-hand stories told by the prophet and the apostles. Each time they made a campfire, the men were captivated by the stick-like device that started the fires so easily.

Early Sunday morning, Ben woke up and noticed the men sitting outside on the point overlooking the magnificent view of the lake. They were praying, reading the Scriptures, and talking softly. As their hosts woke up, they began to join the men on the point. Once a group assembled, Paul began proclaiming the kingdom of God and teaching about the Lord Jesus Christ with all boldness and without hindrance.[3] He was speaking in Greek, but everyone could understand him because they were all wearing their translation devices. If anyone had previously thought the Bible was an ordinary book or Jesus Christ an ordinary person, their minds were completely changed after spending time with these godly men.

After breakfast, Paul went kayaking with Ben. They stayed close to the shoreline as they paddled. Paul said, "Ben, this is a great place, and it has been an incredible adventure with you and everyone here in the future. We have been wondering, though, when do we get to go home? To the past?"

"Tomorrow, Paul. In the morning, the helicopter will pick us up and take us back to Cherry Creek. When Oliver is done with his court case, I will return you all to your own time."

"We will savor our remaining time then. Do you think we can go sailing on that other sailboat, the smaller one?"

"Sure!" Ben smiled. "If the wind picks up, I will arrange it."

That afternoon, the wind indeed came up, and they got

to go on the smaller of the two sailboats. The men took turns because it wasn't big enough for all of them at the same time. They went fast, got wet, had fun, laughed, and gave glory to God.

Chapter 21

The Wrath of Satan

Town Courthouse. Cherry Creek,
Minnesota. Monday morning.

Even though court was not scheduled to reconvene until 9:00 a.m., the townspeople started lining up around six o'clock. At 8:15, the helicopter landed on the baseball field, right in the middle of town. People were everywhere, shaking hands and taking selfies with Matthew, John, Daniel, and Paul. One person was trying to organize a town photo. Most were trying to get family photos with the men. Everyone was excited because they now knew the visitors were not just actors.

To Amy's and Oliver's surprise, it looked as though the townspeople did a pretty good job of keeping the secret! Even though there were many people they did not recognize, there appeared to be no media present. Ben could not stay because he had been called back to pilot the next mission on the time machine. The helicopter pilot took him away to the secret underground base.

In the courtroom, everyone was wearing their Convers8 translation devices and paying attention. The bailiff opened the session. Judge Kane greeted everyone with a big smile and asked Oliver to begin right away. He, too, was much more interested in the witnesses now.

"Thank you, Your Honor. Good morning, ladies and gentlemen of the jury. Today I'm going to provide evidence that the wrath of Satan and the wrath of God are not the same thing. It is important to understand the difference and that the period of great tribulation is not the wrath of God but the wrath of Satan against people who refuse to worship him.[1,2]

"Your Honor, I would like at this time to call to the stand again the apostle John, who wrote the book of Revelation."

Everyone stood and clapped their hands—for several minutes.

Judge Kane called for order, nicely, and said, "Yes, please, go right ahead, Mr. Stuart."

"Thank you, Your Honor. Welcome back, John." Oliver said.

"Thank you, Mr. Stuart. We had a very nice weekend. It's good to be back and see you and Mrs. Stuart again."

"Ladies and gentlemen, as you know, a common belief in our town is that Christians will not have to live through the terrible time of great tribulation, which is commonly and, in my opinion, incorrectly understood as 'the wrath of God.' John is now going to read his story of the wrath of Satan in Revelation 12:6-14. Before he begins, please notice the three things I've listed on the screen that help us identify this as the wrath of Satan taking place during the Great Tribulation."

1. *Verse 6: A period of 1,260 days.*
2. *Verse 9: Satan is cast into the earth.*
3. *Verse 12: The devil is come down, 'having great wrath' and he knows he has a 'short time.'*

"John," Oliver continued, "please read aloud what you wrote in Revelation 12:6-14. We will read along in our exhibit binders and on the screen, Exhibit 31."

"Certainly," John said.

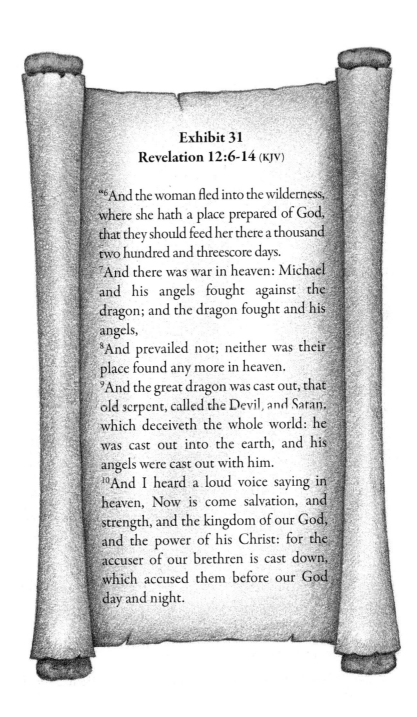

Exhibit 31
Revelation 12:6-14 (KJV)

"⁶And the woman fled into the wilderness, where she hath a place prepared of God, that they should feed her there a thousand two hundred and threescore days.

⁷And there was war in heaven: Michael and his angels fought against the dragon; and the dragon fought and his angels,

⁸And prevailed not; neither was their place found any more in heaven.

⁹And the great dragon was cast out, that old serpent, called the Devil, and Satan, which deceiveth the whole world: he was cast out into the earth, and his angels were cast out with him.

¹⁰And I heard a loud voice saying in heaven, Now is come salvation, and strength, and the kingdom of our God, and the power of his Christ: for the accuser of our brethren is cast down, which accused them before our God day and night.

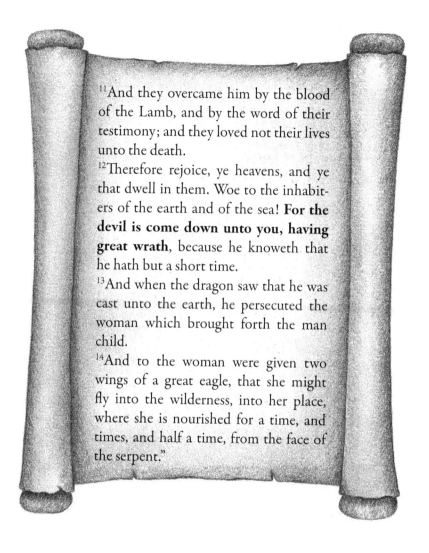

¹¹And they overcame him by the blood of the Lamb, and by the word of their testimony; and they loved not their lives unto the death.

¹²Therefore rejoice, ye heavens, and ye that dwell in them. Woe to the inhabiters of the earth and of the sea! **For the devil is come down unto you, having great wrath**, because he knoweth that he hath but a short time.

¹³And when the dragon saw that he was cast unto the earth, he persecuted the woman which brought forth the man child.

¹⁴And to the woman were given two wings of a great eagle, that she might fly into the wilderness, into her place, where she is nourished for a time, and times, and half a time, from the face of the serpent."

"Thank you, John. Let us review what you just read." He directed everyone to the screen, which read as follows:

1. *The war happens in heaven (verse 7).*

2. *The war is between Michael and his angels and the devil and*

his angels (verse 7).

3. *The devil and his angels are cast out into the earth (verse 9).*

4. *John warns the people of the earth because the devil is coming down, having great wrath (verse 12).*

5. *The devil knows he has a short time (verse 12).*

6. *The devil has three-and-a-half years (verses 6 and 14).*

"Ladies and gentlemen, from this, we can conclude that this war in heaven happens in the middle of the final seven years; and when the dragon, or Satan, is cast onto the earth, he will persecute the woman, symbolizing Israel, which brought forth the man child, symbolizing Jesus Christ. The woman, Israel, will be protected from the face of the serpent for a time, and times, and half a time (a three-and-a-half-year period).

"I would like to remind everyone that John's account agrees with what Jesus said, according to Matthew 24:15-21. Matthew said the Jews living in Judea, which is in the West Bank area will have to run for their lives starting at the time of the Abomination of Desolation because 'then there will be great tribulation, such as was not since the beginning of the world to this time, no, nor ever shall be.'

"As we can see, the three-and-a-half-year tribulation period is actually the wrath of Satan, not the wrath of God, against the Jews, Christians, and anyone else who refuses to take the mark of the beast or worship his image." Oliver turned to the stand. "John, many people have heard the phrase 'the mark of the beast.' Please tell us what that is."

"Very well, Mr. Stuart. The world leader will force everyone to receive a mark on their right hand or on their forehead. If people do not take the mark, they won't be able to buy or sell."

"Thank you, John. I have that for the jurors in their binders, Exhibit 32. Revelation 13:16-18.

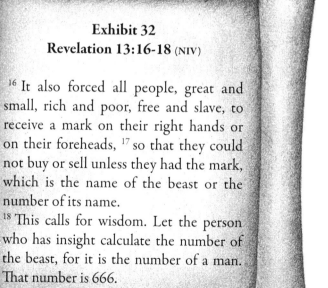

Exhibit 32
Revelation 13:16-18 (NIV)

[16] It also forced all people, great and small, rich and poor, free and slave, to receive a mark on their right hands or on their foreheads, [17] so that they could not buy or sell unless they had the mark, which is the name of the beast or the number of its name.
[18] This calls for wisdom. Let the person who has insight calculate the number of the beast, for it is the number of a man. That number is 666.

"Now we will continue, John, with your explanation and description of the wrath of God, and I will show everyone how it is different from the wrath of Satan."

Chapter 22

The Wrath of God

L adies and gentlemen, now we will define the wrath of God. John, please tell the jurors what exactly this is."

"Very well. The wrath of God is His righteous judgment against man's ungodliness and disobedience. At the end of time as we know it, God's wrath will be poured out by angels in seven vials."[1]

"John, can you be more specific and tell us a little bit about each vial?"

"Very well." As John was speaking, Oliver put up an outline on the screen that read as follows:

God's Wrath:

- *Vial 1: Harmful and painful sores will come upon people who take the mark of the beast and worship his image.*[2]
- *Vial 2: The sea will become like blood, and every living thing in the sea will die.*[3]
- *Vial 3: The rivers and springs of water will become blood.*[4]

- *Vial 4: The sun will scorch people with heat and fire.*[5]
- *Vial 5: Judgment will be poured out on the throne of the beast. Its kingdom will be plunged into darkness. People will gnaw their tongues in anguish and curse the God of heaven for their pain and sores. They will not repent.*[6]
- *Vial 6: The water in the Euphrates River will dry up to prepare the way for the kings from the east, and they will assemble at Armageddon.*[7]
- *Vial 7: A loud voice will come out of the temple, from the throne, saying, 'It is done!' There will be a great earthquake, the biggest ever since time began. The great city will be split into three parts, and the cities of the nations will fall. One-hundred-pound hailstones will fall from heaven on people. Mountains will crumble.*[8]

As John finished describing the vials, Oliver thanked him and turned to the jury. "Ladies and gentlemen, the King James translation says, 'the vials of the wrath of God.' Other translations say 'the seven bowls.' John, please read Exhibit 33, regarding what you wrote about the vials, or the wrath of God."

"Certainly." John read Exhibit 33 from the iPad in his language. The jurors followed along in their exhibit binders. The King James and the English Standard translations were provided for comparison and were also up on the screen.

Exhibit 33a
Revelation 16:1-2 (KJV)

"¹And I heard a great voice out of the temple saying to the seven angels, Go your ways, and pour out the **vials of the wrath of God** upon the earth.
²And the first went, and poured out his vial upon the earth; and there fell a noisome and grievous sore upon the men which had the mark of the beast, and upon them which worshipped his image."

Exhibit 33b
Revelation 16:1-2 (ESV)

"¹Then I heard a loud voice from the temple telling the seven angels, 'Go and pour out on the earth the **seven bowls of the wrath of God.**'
²So the first angel went and poured out his bowl on the earth, and harmful and painful sores came upon the people who bore the mark of the beast and worshiped its image."

"Thank you, John. Ladies and gentlemen of the jury, the 'vials' or 'bowls' are the wrath of God. The first vial, or bowl, is poured out on the people who take the mark of the beast and worship his image. Therefore, we can conclude that the Antichrist has to be revealed and the mark of the beast has to be implemented before the vials, or the wrath of God, can be poured out.

"Earlier, I provided evidence that the 'wrath of Satan' is described as a three-and-a-half-year period, simultaneous with the Great Tribulation. The world leader, the Antichrist, will have control over a big portion of the earth, seeking to destroy Jews, Christians, and anyone else who refuses to worship him and take his mark.

"In contrast, looking at the vials of God's wrath, it is clear that the vials will be poured out at the end of the final seven years, most likely upon the armies invading Jerusalem at the Battle of Armageddon.[9] Bibles will be passed out now so that you can read the full account from John in context, in Revelation 16:1-21.

"If we examine closely vial seven, verse 19, John specifically says 'his wrath,' referring to God. So, again, we have further verification that the vials are the wrath of God. The verse is in your binder, Exhibit 34."

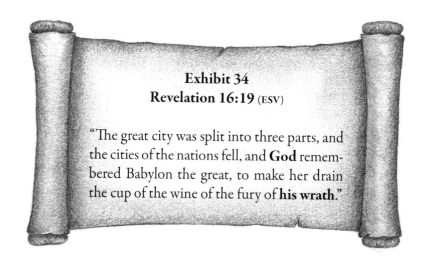

Exhibit 34
Revelation 16:19 (ESV)

"The great city was split into three parts, and the cities of the nations fell, and **God** remembered Babylon the great, to make her drain the cup of the wine of the fury of **his wrath**."

Confirmation of the Covenant — Abomination of Desolation — Jesus Returns / Vials Poured Out

"Your Honor," Oliver continued, "I have no further questions for this witness."

Judge Kane responded, "John, thank you very much for coming to our town. It's an honor to have met you and the others. You may step down. Court is now in recess. We will reconvene at 1:30 p.m. for closing arguments."

The townspeople had arranged for a community potluck lunch. People continued taking pictures and giving hugs to Paul, John, Daniel, and Matthew. They all kept their translation devices in so they could communicate directly. Once people were seated and eating, there was a question-and-answer time. The townspeople directed their questions to one or more of the four men. This continued for about an hour until the mysterious time machine suddenly appeared. When the doors opened, Ben and the time-traveling team came out and greeted everyone.

The crew had departed the secret base headquarters for their next mission, but Ben had switched the date and GPS coordinates to go back in time just fifteen minutes so that they could pick up Matthew, John, Paul, and Daniel and return them to their own respective times before continuing on with their new assignment.

The time machine now had everyone's attention. They were so excited. Everyone pulled out their cell phones again. People lined up to take family pictures in front of the machine. They also lined up to go inside the machine. Ben gave mini-tours, but no pictures were allowed inside.

Soon it was time to say goodbyes. After sharing tears, laughter, and more hugs, the men entered the machine and waved their final goodbyes to the crowd. The doors closed, and forty-five seconds later, the time machine disappeared.

Amy said to Oliver, "Bible study in this town will never be the same again."

"What an experience! Will the men remember any of this when they get back home?"

"No, Ben says they won't remember," Amy said.

"Incredible! How come you didn't go with Ben and the others on this trip?"

"Someone else wanted to take my spot. I was fine with that. The more people that get to have the experience, the better."

Chapter 23

The Time of the End

Everyone returned to the courtroom by 1:30 p.m. The bailiff announced, "All rise. Court is now in session, the Honorable Judge Kane presiding."

"Mr. Stuart, are you ready for your closing arguments?"

"Yes, Your Honor," Oliver said.

"Very well then, you may begin."

"Thank you, Your Honor.

"Ladies and gentlemen of the jury, in addition to the pre-tribulation view and the post-tribulation view, we know there is a third group of people in our town who believe we can't necessarily know the future and that time will just continue on as usual. They believe we will grow old and die like our grandparents did, and the 'end time' will be several generations from now.

"However, God told Daniel to 'shut up the words and seal the book, until the time of the end.'¹ In other words, in the time of the end, the book will be unsealed, and the people who are paying attention and living during that time will understand the prophecies in the Bible and see them come to pass.

"Please refer to your exhibit binders one last time, to Exhibit 35, as I quote our friend, Daniel." Oliver read the exhibit aloud.

Exhibit 35
Daniel 12:1-4 (ESV)

"¹At that time shall arise Michael, the great prince who has charge of your people. And there shall be a time of trouble, such as never has been since there was a nation till that time. But at that time your people shall be delivered, everyone whose name shall be found written in the book. ² And many of those who sleep in the dust of the earth shall awake, some to everlasting life, and some to shame and everlasting contempt. ³ And those who are wise shall shine like the brightness of the sky above; and those who turn many to righteousness, like the stars forever and ever. ⁴ But you, Daniel, shut up the words and seal the book, **until the time of the end.** Many shall run to and fro, and knowledge shall increase."

"Ladies and gentlemen," Oliver said, "God is truly unlocking the mysteries and unsealing the book of the end-time world events. One of our witnesses, Dr. Sarah Anderson, from the Institute for Advanced Prophetic Studies, told us about Irvin Baxter and Endtime Ministries. Pastor Baxter is one of the people I believe God is using to unseal the book in our present time.

"At the beginning of these proceedings, I said I was going to convince you beyond a shadow of a doubt that according to the Bible, there are specific events which must take place before the rapture of the church. I explained these events in detail so that you would be able to recognize them when you see them, and I also presented compelling evidence for the precise timing of the rapture. On the screen I have listed for you the ten events that my key witnesses and I have proven must happen before the rapture."

1. *Falling away / Rebellion (2 Thessalonians 2:3)*
2. *Confirmation of the Covenant or Peace Agreement (Daniel 9:27)*
3. *The sixth trumpet, killing one-third of people on earth (Revelation 9:13-15)*
4. *Third Temple built in Jerusalem (2 Thessalonians 2:3-4)*
5. *Antichrist revealed and claims to be God (2 Thessalonians 2:4; Abomination of Desolation)—he stops animal sacrifices (Daniel 9:27)*
6. *Jews living in Judea run for their lives (Matt. 24:16-20)*
7. *A period of great tribulation, wrath of Satan, mark of beast implemented (Matthew 24:29-31, Revelation 20:4)*

8. *Two Witnesses prophesy for 1,260 days (Revelation 11:3)*
9. *Two Witnesses die, lie in the street for three-and-a-half days (Revelation 11:7-9)*
10. *The Dead in Christ rise first [are raptured] (1 Thessalonians 4:16)*

After offering those in attendance a moment to review the list, Oliver continued. "There are actually more than ten prophecies in the Bible that need to occur before the rapture of the church. If anyone here would like more information about the end-time prophecies, please see me after the trial.

"So, Your Honor, ladies and gentlemen of the jury, guests of the court—it's time for you to decide for yourselves. Are you gearing up to disappear? Or are you gearing up to participate in the greatest revival the world has ever seen?

"Daniel wrote: 'They that understand among the people shall instruct many' (Daniel 11:33 KJV). Now you are among the people who understand and shall instruct many. So, as Jesus himself said: 'Go and make disciples of all nations, baptizing them in the name of the Father and of the Son and of the Holy Spirit, teaching them to observe all that I have commanded you. And behold, I am with you always, to the end of the age' (Matthew 28:19-20, ESV). That is all, Your Honor. I rest my case."

"Thank you, Mr. Stuart. Jury members, as a reminder, we explained at the beginning of this trial that no crime had been committed but that members of our community requested a formal setting for each side to present its case, without interruption by the opposing side, as would normally occur in a real court case. As you know, we chose six jurors who take the pre-tribulation rapture position and six jurors who believe that we will all be here and raptured at the end of the tribulation period. Ms. Norton made her case that Jesus Christ will rapture His church at any moment, beginning the terrible tribulation period and the final seven years to the Battle of Armageddon. When Mr. Stuart began, he stated that he would present evidence that would overwhelmingly convince you, beyond a shadow of a doubt, that there are specific events that must take place before the rapture of the church. He also stated that he would present compelling evidence for the precise timing of the rapture of the church. Soon, you will move to the jury room and discuss the evidence presented. Please return when you have completed your deliberation and are ready to render your verdict. Does the biblical evidence support the pre-tribulation rapture position? Or, does it support a post-tribulation rapture? Court is now adjourned, and the jury is dismissed to deliberate."

As people exited the courtroom, Lucy stayed behind. She wanted to ask Oliver more about Bible prophecies.

"Hello, Oliver."

"Hi, Lucy. How are you and your family?"

"We are well, thank you."

"Is there something I can help you with?"

"Well, yes. You brought up a lot of very convincing points during your case. I was not particularly interested in the 'end times' or the prophecies before this week. You said if we wanted more information about the prophecies, we should talk to you after the trial."

A few more people started gathering around Oliver as well, inquiring about the information he had offered.

"Yes, of course," he said as he began walking out of the courtroom towards his car. "Most of the information I presented to you in court I learned from Irvin Baxter, through his DVDs, his daily online show, and *EndTime* magazine."

"Daily online show?" Lucy inquired.

"It's called *End of the Age*. It used to be called *Politics and Religion*. I like tuning in on a regular basis because they discuss current world events and how they are connected to the prophecies."

When he got to his car, he threw his Reederang vintage leather briefcase on the front seat and then opened his trunk. Lucy and the people that had followed him saw a stack of *EndTime* magazines along with boxes of DVDs, all organized according to title.

"Here you go," Oliver said, handing a DVD to Lucy. "This one is called *United States Discovered in the Bible*. It's the first in a series of fourteen. You can borrow it and give it back to me when you're done."

"Oh my goodness, Oliver! Why do you have all of this in your trunk?"

"Well, I lend them out to people, and sometimes, I give them away. I keep a supply on hand so I won't run out. Here, take a magazine with you too. You can keep it or pass it along to someone else when you are done reading it."

Others started asking if they could borrow DVDs, and Oliver gladly passed them out. A few people, however, said they didn't have a DVD player. So, Oliver told them about the *End of the Age+* streaming app where they could get access to the series along with many previous and new releases.

"Thanks, Oliver!" Lucy said. "This is all very interesting. I will watch it and get it back to you soon."

The others agreed, "Yes, thank you, Oliver," they said.

Chapter 24

A Time for Decision

While they waited for the jury to return, Holly and Oliver went to the local diner together. Holly ordered tea, Oliver coffee. They had gone round and round with each other for years, each believing that his or her view was biblically "right." Even though they were on opposite sides during the trial, they shared the excitement and the privilege of meeting a few of the people God chose to write the Bible.

Holly said, "Ollie, I listened to everything you said, and I still believe you are wrong. I still believe the rapture can happen any day now. But, let's just say for a second that you are right and that we have to wait for the signing of a peace agreement between Israel and the Palestinians, and then we have to live through the final seven years to the Battle of Armageddon. Why is it so important for you to convince people of this? What difference does it make? A lot of people don't care one way or the other when the rapture will happen."

"I'm okay with people not agreeing with me," her brother answered. "But I do want them to know the prophecies so that when they see them happening in the world, they will be aware and recognize what's going on, and perhaps even be a bit excited like I am. It's exciting to watch the Bible happen in real time. If people read a book that was written over two thousand years ago and then see the events written in the book being played out on the world scene in our present time, that has to get their attention. If God wrote things in the Bible that will happen in the future, then He wants us to know these things in advance for a reason.

"As to what difference does it make? Well, what if I told you that at some point, there is going to be a one-world government and a world dictator ruling over this one-world government, who might be compared to someone like Adolf Hitler, only much worse. Would that concern you?"

Holly responded, "Of course. But I don't think I will be here when the Antichrist shows up. I believe we will already be raptured."

"Well, let's just say for a minute that the post-tribulation view is correct and that we haven't been raptured yet. This time, it isn't just Jewish people who will be persecuted. The Antichrist will 'make war with the saints'[1] and anyone else who refuses to take his mark and worship his image. According to the Bible, the people who don't take the mark and worship his image won't be able to buy or sell.[2] If we know these things are going to happen in advance, we won't be caught off guard. We can use the prophecies to share Christ with others and help them prepare for eternity."

"Okay, Ollie. Let's say what you believe is true. Then how are we supposed to survive during that time when we can't buy or sell?"

A couple passing through town was seated at the table next to Holly and Oliver. They had ordered burgers, fries, and milkshakes. They were unaware of the court case and the special guests who had left a short while ago in the time machine. But, they could not help overhearing the conversation between Holly and Oliver.

Oliver answered, "The Bible doesn't guarantee survival, Holly. Everyone has a birth date and a death date. The question is, where are they going to spend eternity? Heaven or hell? One can die any time: today, tomorrow, next week, next year, before the Great Tribulation, or, yes, even during the Great Tribulation. Is our goal to survive? Or should our goal be to see how many people we can take with us to heaven? Paul wrote to Timothy, 'In the last days perilous times will come,'[3] and 'all who desire to live a godly life in Christ Jesus will be persecuted.'[4] There is good news, though. The Antichrist will have enemies, and he won't have control over every nation.[5,6]

"One more point, Holly, is that some people believe the Bible is just an old book and that it has no relevance in today's world whatsoever, not for one's personal life here on earth or for after one dies. I like showing people something that will happen in the future, even if they disagree with me. Then, when the event happens sometime down the road, they will be more interested in what the Bible has to say about the prophecies and, most importantly, its relevance to their own lives."

The man at the next table turned to Oliver and said, "Excuse me, um, sorry to interrupt. I'm Andrew, and this is my wife, Kate. We couldn't help but overhear your conversation. Did you just say the Bible foretells the future?"

"Nice to meet you. I'm Oliver. This is my sister Holly . . . and yes, I did say that. Would you like to join us at our table?"

Andrew looked at Kate, who smiled and said, "Sure, thank you."

Oliver said, "Where are you from?"

Kate smiled, "We are from Canada—Calgary, actually. We're taking the summer to travel the United States."

"Oh, that sounds like so much fun! Is that your camper?" Holly asked, pointing out the window.

"Yes, we've been having a great time," Kate replied. "You were talking about some pretty serious stuff: eternity, death dates, heaven and hell, eh?"

Andrew finished her thought. "Persecution, the Antichrist, and perilous times. You have to admit, that isn't something you hear people talking about every day."

Holly smiled and said, "I suppose that's true. We both happen to be very interested in Bible prophecies and how they pertain to our lives. What about you guys? What do you know about the Bible?"

Andrew answered, "Well, my folks dropped me off at church when I was a kid pretty much every Sunday. I've heard all kinds of Bible stories. I attended youth group in high school, but after I started university, I never got too involved in church."

Looking at Kate, Holly asked, "How about you?"

"Well, I know that Jesus is God's Son, and I know John 3:16: 'For God so loved the world, that He gave His only Son, that whoever believes in Him should not perish but have eternal life.' I know that if we believe in Him, we will go to heaven when we die."

"You are right, Kate. The Bible does say that," Holly responded. "Think about this, though. If one just acknowledges the fact that Jesus is God's Son, and they 'believe' in Him in this sense, do they get to go to heaven when they die? For example, Satan acknowledges that Jesus is God's Son. Do you think he will spend eternity in heaven because he 'believes' in Jesus?"

"Whoa, that's an interesting point," Andrew responded. "So, how does a person get to go to heaven when they die?"

Oliver pulled out his phone to read three scriptures. "Jesus answered that question himself in John 3:3. He says, 'Truly, truly, I say to you, unless one is born again he cannot see the kingdom of God.' Then He says in John 3:5, 'Unless one is born of water and the Spirit, he cannot enter the kingdom of God.' Again in John 14:6, Jesus says, 'I am the way, and the truth, and the life. No one comes to the Father except through me.'"

Kate asked, "So, what exactly does that mean?"

Holly got very excited to share her faith. She explained with a big smile, "Being born again is when God convicts you of your sin.[7] You repent and turn your life over to Him as Lord.[8] The Spirit of God comes to live inside you.[9] You become a child of the living God.[10] You obey Him, not because you have to, but because you truly desire to please Him.[11] You realize the magnitude of what Jesus did for you when He died on the cross for your sins so that you wouldn't have to spend eternity in hell, and this gives you a joy of living each day for His glory.[12] You become more like Him the more time you spend in prayer, reading His word and in worship.[13] You are not your own anymore, you were bought with a price.[14] Being born again is saying to God every day, 'God, take my life, and make me into the person You want me to be.'"[15]

Andrew chimed in, "Hang on a second. We believe in Jesus, but what you're talking about sounds foreign to what Kate and I have experienced. Religion to me is a list of dos and don'ts, not a relationship with God such as you describe. It also sounds like a huge commitment and a lot of work. It sounds like what you are saying is that once you are born again, everything in your life revolves around God. I'm not sure I agree with that. I think God is good and that He lets good people go to heaven."

Oliver asked, "Andrew, do you consider yourself to be a good person?"

"Of course." He answered.

"Let me ask you this, Andrew, if you died today and God judged you by the Ten Commandments, would you go to heaven?"

"Yes, I believe so."

"Tell me, Andrew, how many lies have you told in your life?"

"Um, too many to count."

"So, what does that make you?"

"A liar I guess, eh?"

"The Bible says, 'All liars shall have their part in the lake which burneth with fire and brimstone.'[16] Have you ever stolen anything?"

Andrew answered, not as confident now, "Maybe. Well, actually, yes. I have stolen things."

"What does that make you?"

"I don't know . . . a thief?"

"Have you ever used the Lord's name as a cuss word?"

"What do you mean?"

"Well, do you ever say 'Jesus Christ' as a swear word? Or, maybe you drop the 'Christ' and just say 'Jesus' as an expression of anger. How about 'Oh my God!' or 'OMG'? Do you ever say that?"

"Sure, but everybody does. It's just a phrase people say."

"Do you know the second commandment?"

"Not sure. What does it say?"

"It says in Deuteronomy 5:11, 'the LORD will not leave him unpunished who takes His name in vain.'"[17]

"Oh, I never thought about that before."

"Tell me this, Andrew, 'Have you ever lusted after another woman?'"

He looked at Kate, not wanting to answer. "Sure. But doesn't everyone do that?"

"Jesus says that anyone 'who looks at a woman with lustful intent has already committed adultery with her in his heart.'[18]

"Andrew, how do you treat your parents? Have you always honored your folks? Do you treat them in a way that is respectful and pleasing to God?"

"Well, no, not always."

"So, Andrew, by your own admission, you are a liar, a thief, you use the Lord's name in vain, which is blasphemy, you are an adulterer at heart, and you dishonor your parents. That's five of the Ten Commandments. If God judges you by the Ten Commandments on the Day of Judgment, will you be innocent or guilty?"

"Well, it looks like I might be guilty according to your line of thinking."

Oliver gently asked, "Do you think you will go to heaven or hell?"

"I'm not sure."

"Imagine this, Andrew. You are standing in a court of law, guilty of a serious crime. There is a $100,000 fine. The judge says, 'You are guilty. Do you have anything to say before I pass sentence?' You answer, 'Yes, judge. I'm sorry for what I have done. Please forgive me.' Can a good judge let you go simply because you say you are sorry or that you won't do it again?"

"No, I guess not."

"Of course not. There is a $100,000 fine that must be paid. However, if someone pays the fine for you, can the judge then let you go?"

"That sounds right."

"Once the fine has been paid, your debt to the law has been satisfied, and the judge can set you free. In the same way, each of us is guilty before God, and He will not let us go simply because we say we're sorry. Of course, we should be sorry. However, the fine for our crime must still be paid.[19] There are two points here, Andrew. The first is that we are all sinful and therefore rightfully deserve to go to hell when we die."

"It sounds like I'm going to hell when I die."

"Does that concern you?"

Andrew, humbling himself a bit, replied, "Yes, that concerns me. But you said there are two points?"

"Yes! Do you know what the God of the universe did for you so that you wouldn't have to spend eternity in hell?"

Kate interjected, "I know! He sent His Son, Jesus, to die on the cross."

Holly confirmed, "Yes, that is correct. The second point is that the fine was paid! God provided a way for us to be forgiven. The question is, how do you access this forgiveness?"

Andrew asked, "Well, what's the answer?"

Holly answered, "Jesus suffered and died in your place, taking your punishment for you so that you can live. You broke the Law, and Jesus paid your fine. He lived a righteous life to satisfy the Law and imputes His righteousness to us. Then Jesus rose from the dead and defeated death. If you will repent—turn away from sin—and place your trust in Jesus Christ alone as your Savior, God will forgive you and grant you everlasting life.

He will change you from the inside out and make you a new person in Christ."[20]

Oliver added, "Yes, and God offers complete forgiveness of sin and the gift of everlasting life *freely* to those who will surrender everything to Him through faith in Jesus Christ."[21]

Holly asked, "Does this make sense to you guys?"

Andrew and Kate both nodded their heads and said yes at the same time.

"Are you ready to turn from your sins and trust Jesus for your eternal salvation?" Oliver asked.

Kate responded, "I am. Absolutely. How do I do that?"

Holly answered, "You can talk to God right now. Confess your sins and turn from them, placing your trust in Jesus as Lord and Savior—surrendering your life to Him."

Oliver turned to Andrew, "How about you, Andrew? What are you thinking?"

Just then, Holly and Oliver both received a text telling them that the verdict was in. They needed to get back to court.

Oliver said, "Um, listen, we need to go. May I suggest you walk over to the park after you are done eating? Find a bench, talk to each other, and talk to God. If you are ready, Andrew, pray with your wife. Ask God for forgiveness, surrender your lives to Him, and invite Him to change you from the inside out."

Kate looked at Holly, "Wait, you can't leave us. What if we pray wrong?"

Looking at her phone, Holly asked Kate, "What is your number?"

While Oliver was giving his business card to Andrew, he answered Kate's question, "Don't worry, you can't pray wrong. Prayer is just talking to God. He knows your heart. He knows if you are sincere or not."

Kate said, "But . . . how will we know if God comes into our lives?"

Holly answered as they were walking away, "You'll know . . . and I will text you a few verses. If you are staying in town tonight, we can meet up with you later this evening if you want, or even tomorrow."

"Yes, definitely," said Kate.

Holly and Oliver prayed as they walked back to court.

"Dear Lord," Oliver prayed, "thank you for opening the hearts and minds of Andrew and Kate. We ask you, in the name of Jesus, to move in their hearts, convict them of their sin, show them how they have offended you and violated your Law, and cause them both to cry out to you for salvation. Thank you for giving us the privilege to share with them today."

Holly asked Oliver, "What do you think is going to happen?"

"With Andrew and Kate?"

"No . . . with the jury."

"I don't know, Holly, but either way, we must stay focused on sharing the gospel of Christ. That's the most important thing, and I think we both agree."

"Amen to that, Ollie! It's pretty great how God designed each life for a specific purpose, that He didn't create anyone in error or by mistake, and that He has a plan for each one of us to follow while we live here on earth."

"Do you remember that song we used to sing when we were kids, 'Father, I adore you, lay my life before you. How I love you?'"

"I do! I always liked that song. It's a great prayer, too."

Oliver and Holly entered the courthouse.

Later on, Andrew and Kate were in the park, holding hands, bowing their heads in prayer.

"There is rejoicing in the presence of the angels
of God over one sinner who repents."
— Luke 15:10 (NIV)

Discussion Questions

1. Which of the following characters do you relate with most, and why?
   a. Oliver
   b. Holly
   c. Lucy
   d. Andrew
   e. Kate

2. Think about what it would be like to spend time with Daniel, Matthew, Luke, or Paul. What question(s) would you ask them?

3. Before reading this book, what were your thoughts about the end times and the rapture?

4. Has your view of the end times changed? If so, how?

5. What compelling evidence did Oliver present for a post-tribulation rapture?

6. Do you agree with Oliver, that there are specific events that must take place before the rapture of the church? Why, or why not?

7. Oliver and Holly may disagree on the timing of the rapture, but they agree that sharing the gospel is important, no matter what. Think about their conversation with Andrew and Kate. What was your favorite point or example from that conversation, and why?

8. Did you know before you read this book that the sixth trumpet will result in the death of one-third of the people on earth? Does this give you an urgency to share the gospel with others?

9. According to Oliver, how will we know when the final seven years begin?

10. Each of us has an individual relationship with God through Jesus Christ. What do you hear God saying to you, specifically, through this book?

The Temple Mount

The Temple Mount, Jerusalem, Israel, 2015

These pictures show an area big enough to build the third temple on the Temple Mount north of the Dome of the Rock. It will be structured similar to the second temple, which was destroyed in 70 A.D.

(Photos by Kelli Nelson)

At the Temple Institute Visitors Center in the Jewish Quarter, Old City, Jerusalem, guests can see a model of the second temple, as well as a replica of the Ark of the Covenant and many other items created for use in the new temple once it's built.

The Euphrates River

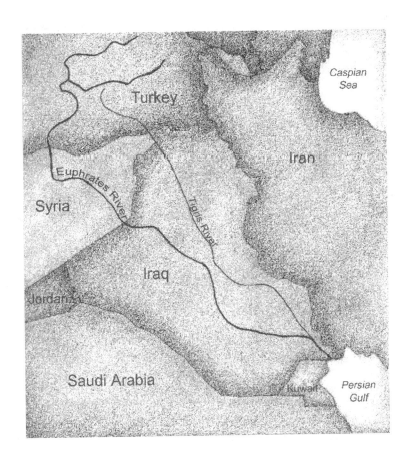

The Sixth Trumpet and the Euphrates River are connected in the same Scripture passage, indicating the war will begin in this region. John heard the number of troops.

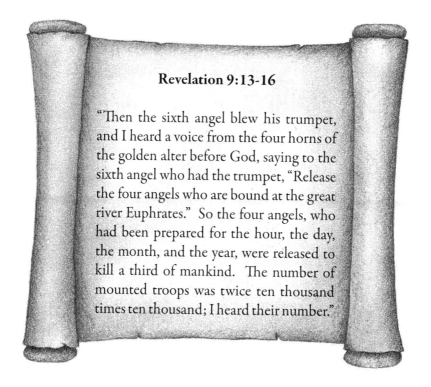

Revelation 9:13-16

"Then the sixth angel blew his trumpet, and I heard a voice from the four horns of the golden alter before God, saying to the sixth angel who had the trumpet, "Release the four angels who are bound at the great river Euphrates." So the four angels, who had been prepared for the hour, the day, the month, and the year, were released to kill a third of mankind. The number of mounted troops was twice ten thousand times ten thousand; I heard their number."

Where is Judea?

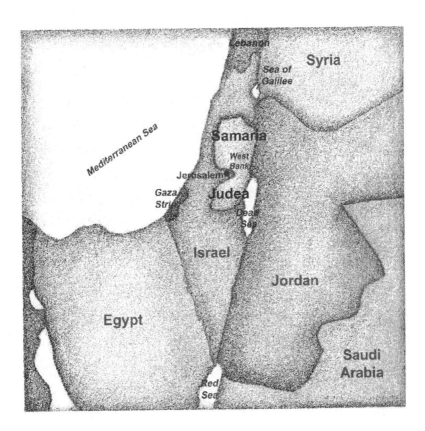

"...let those who are in Judea flee..."

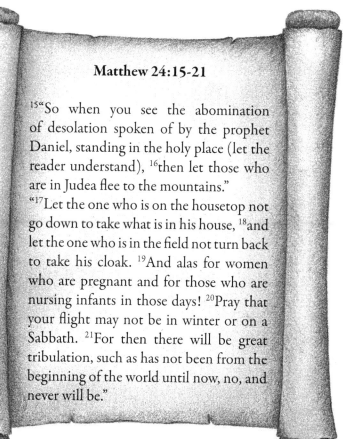

Matthew 24:15-21

[15]"So when you see the abomination of desolation spoken of by the prophet Daniel, standing in the holy place (let the reader understand), [16]then let those who are in Judea flee to the mountains."

"[17]Let the one who is on the housetop not go down to take what is in his house, [18]and let the one who is in the field not turn back to take his cloak. [19]And alas for women who are pregnant and for those who are nursing infants in those days! [20]Pray that your flight may not be in winter or on a Sabbath. [21]For then there will be great tribulation, such as has not been from the beginning of the world until now, no, and never will be."

Addendum

On January 28, 2020, US President Donald Trump released his proposal for Middle East peace between the Palestinian and Israeli people. Many nations have voiced their support for the Trump peace plan, also referred to as the "Deal of the Century." The question presents itself: Does the proposed peace plan meet the biblical requirements necessary to qualify as "the" peace plan, or the Confirmation of the Covenant, as defined in our story?

At the time of this writing, the "Deal of the Century" is published on the White House website and can be read at whitehouse.gov.* The official name is called "Peace to Prosperity – A Vision to Improve the Lives of the Palestinian and Israeli People."

According to Irvin Baxter, end time Bible prophecy teacher, four out of the five prophesied criteria are specifically mentioned in the proposal. One element, however, the building of the third Jewish temple, is not addressed either way. The proposal doesn't say it can be built, but it also doesn't say that it can't be built. So when all is said and done, if permission is given for the third Jewish temple to

---

* https://trumpwhitehouse.archives.gov/wp-content/uploads/2020/01/Peace-to-Prosperity-0120.pdf

be built, Donald Trump's peace plan will match up perfectly with the biblical requirements necessary to qualify as the Confirmation of the Covenant as defined in our story.

The following analysis is used with permission from Endtime Ministries' March/April 2020 issue of EndTime magazine, summarizing the five biblical criteria and comparing them to the proposed "Deal of the Century."

1. A Palestinian State in Judea

Matthew 24:15-16, 21
"When ye therefore shall see the abomination of desolation, spoken of by Daniel the prophet, stand in the holy place, (whoso readeth, let him understand):
Then let them which be in Judaea flee into the mountains . . .
For then shall be great tribulation, such as was not since the beginning of the world to this time, no, nor ever shall be."

Jesus foretold an event called the Abomination of Desolation. Other passages clearly say this event will happen three-and-a-half years after the Palestinian-Israeli peace agreement is signed. He warns that Jews who are living in Judea will have to flee for their lives. Obviously, Judea will be under enemy control by that time.

Proposed Peace Plan: "Deal of the Century" – Page 12

This Vision is a fair compromise and contemplates a Palestinian state that encompasses territory reasonably comparable in size to the territory of the West Bank (Judea) and Gaza pre-1967. Note: The map accompanying Trump's peace plan shows the vast majority of the new Palestinian state will be in Judea.

2. Jews Can Stay in the New Palestinian State

Matthew 24:15-16

This passage clearly states there will be Jews living in Judea at the time of the Abomination of Desolation, which will occur three and one-half years after the Palestinian-Israeli peace agreement.

Proposed Peace Plan: "Deal of the Century" – Page 12

The Israeli population located in enclaves that remain inside contiguous Palestinian territory but that are part of the State of Israel shall have the option to remain in place unless they choose otherwise and maintain their existing Israeli citizenship. Note: This describes Israelis living inside the new Palestinian state being able to stay there while still being citizens of Israel.

3. Temple Mount Will Be Shared

Revelation 11:1-2
"¹And there was given me a reed like unto a rod: and
the angel stood, saying, Rise, and measure the temple

of God, and the altar, and them that worship therein.
²But the court which is without the temple leave out, and
measure it not; for it is given unto the Gentiles: and the holy
city shall they tread under foot forty and two months."

Note: This passage paints a picture of a temple with Jewish worshippers on the Temple Mount. Then John was told not to measure the outer court of the temple because it would be under Gentile control during the last half of the Final Seven Years.

Proposed Peace Plan: "Deal of the Century" – Page 16

Jerusalem's holy sites should remain open and available for peaceful worshippers and tourists of all faiths. People of every faith should be permitted to pray on the Temple Mount/Haram al-Sharif, in a manner that is fully respectful to their religion, taking into account the times of each religion's prayers and holidays, as well as other religious factors.

4. A Jewish Temple Will Be Built on the Temple Mount

2 Thessalonians 2:3-4
"³Let no man deceive you by any means: for that day
shall not come, except there come a falling away first, and
that man of sin be revealed, the son of perdition; ⁴Who
opposeth and exalteth himself above all that is called
God, or that is worshipped; so that he as God sitteth in
the temple of God, shewing himself that he is God."

This passage describes the Antichrist sitting in the temple of God. He obviously couldn't sit in the temple if there were no temple to sit in. In Revelation 11:1 above, John was told to measure the temple. He obviously could not do that if there were no temple to measure.

Proposed Peace Plan: "Deal of the Century" – Page 16

The "Deal of the Century" does not comment on the building of the temple one way or the other. However, it does say that people "should be permitted to pray on the Temple Mount in a manner that is fully respectful to their religion."

The Jews believe their religion requires them to build a temple on the Temple Mount. They already have all the furniture, utensils and architectural drawings in preparation for the building of their temple. The Jewish people will not sign a final agreement that does not provide a path for them to rebuild their temple, which was destroyed by the Romans in 70 A.D.

5. Israel Will Control an Undivided Jerusalem

Zechariah 14:2
"For I will gather all nations against Jerusalem to battle; and the city shall be taken, and the houses rifled, and the women ravished; and half of the city shall go forth into captivity, and the residue of the people shall not be cut off from the city."

Zechariah 14:2 describes the Battle of Armageddon. It states that half of Jerusalem will go into captivity to the armies of the Antichrist during Armageddon. This indicates that all of Jerusalem will have been under Israeli control until Armageddon.

Proposed Peace Plan: "Deal of the Century" – Page 17

Jerusalem will remain the sovereign capital of the State of Israel and it should remain an undivided city. The sovereign capital of the State of Palestine should be in the section of East Jerusalem located in all areas east and north of the existing security barrier, including Kafr Aqab, the eastern part of Shuafat and Abu Dis, and could be named Al Quds or another name as determined by the State of Palestine.

Note: This will leave the Temple Mount, the Kidron Valley and the Mount of Olives all under Israeli control.

Prophesied Peace Agreement	President Trump's Proposed Peace Plan
A Palestinian state in Judea	A Palestinian state in Judea
Jews can stay in the new Palestinian state	Jews can stay in the new Palestinian state
Temple Mount will be shared	Temple Mount will be shared
A Jewish temple will be built on the Temple Mount	Does not mention whether a temple will be built or not
Israel will control an undivided Jerusalem	Israel will control an undivided Jerusalem

As we can see, the Peace to Prosperity proposal matches up very closely with Bible prophecies. We know that at some point in the future, when negotiations are finished and the deal is signed, a pathway will be provided for the Jewish people to rebuild their temple on the Temple Mount. I agree with Irvin Baxter that when this happens, the foretold event referred to as the Confirmation of the Covenant will present itself as a Palestinian-Israeli peace agreement and will mark the beginning of a final seven-year period that will end with the Battle of Armageddon and the physical return of Jesus Christ to the earth.

Frequently Asked Questions

Answered by Endtime Ministries DVDs and podcasts, available at www.endtime.com.

1. When is the marriage supper of the Lamb?
End of the Age podcast January 2, 2019, 49:30 minutes into the show. "The Coming End Time Revival 1." https://www.endtime.com/end-of-the-age/end-time-revival/

2. Where is the church mentioned in Revelation after chapter four, verse one?
End of the Age podcast January 2, 2019, 47 minutes into the show through marker 52:29. "The Coming End Time Revival 1." https://www.endtime.com/end-of-the-age/end-time-revival/

3. How many times in the book of Revelation is the rapture described?
End of the Age podcast January 2, 2019, 47 minutes into the show through marker 52:29 (specifically 50:35-52:25). "The Coming End Time Revival 1." https://www.endtime.com/end-of-the-age/end-time-revival/

4. Why will the peace agreement only be temporary?
Understanding the ENDTIME Lesson 6 DVD, Israel - God's Prophetic Time Clock.

Also: End of the Age podcast February 20, 2019, 17:40 minutes into the show through marker 19:10. "Middle East Update."

Also: End of the Age podcast March 4, 2019, 12:53 minutes into the show through marker 13:30. "Peace Plan Update." https://www.endtime.com/end-of-the-age/peace-plan-update-3/

Also: The peace agreement will be a seven-year temporary agreement because "the status of Jerusalem will be left unresolved." EndTime magazine, issue July/Aug 2017 page 10 under the heading "Summarizing the Peace Agreement."

5. Who is protecting Israel (the woman) during the Great Tribulation, Revelation 12:14?
The Eagle is the symbol for the United States. The United States of America will be protecting Israel.

Understanding the ENDTIME Lesson 1 DVD, United States Discovered in the Bible.

Also: End of the Age podcast February 4, 2019, 25:40 minutes into the show. "Peace Plan Update."
https://www.endtime.com/end-of-the-age/peace-plan-update/

Also: End of the Age podcast February 8, 2019, 40:07 minutes into the show through marker 41:05. "Open Line 327." https://www.endtime.com/end-of-the-age/open-line-327/

6. How do we know there will be a one-world government in the end times? Which countries will be included? Not included?
Understanding the ENDTIME Lesson 2, New World Order Is World Government.

Also: End of the Age podcast February 18, 2019, 2:55 minutes into the show through marker 4:50. "Globalism vs. National Sovereignty."
https://www.endtime.com/end-of-the-age/globalism-vs-national -sovereignty/

Also: End of the Age podcast February 8, 2019, 39:36 minutes into the show. "Open Line 327."
https://www.endtime.com/end-of-the-age/open-line-327/

7. Will there be any countries that will not be under the control of the Antichrist?
Yes–Israel, Jordan, and the United States of America. The United States of America will not be included in the one-world government.

End of the Age podcast February 8, 2019, 39:36 minutes into the show through marker 41:05. "Open Line 327." https://www. endtime.com/end-of-the-age/open-line-327/

Also: End of the Age podcast August 28, 2019, 53:20 into the show through marker 56:01. "Arab Minister Willing to Join Moderate Left-Wing Government in Israel." https://www.end-time.com/end-of-the-age/arab-minister-willing-to-join-moderate-left-wing-government-in-israel/

8. Where will the Antichrist come from?
Understanding the ENDTIME Lesson 7 DVD, Holy Roman Empire Reborn.

Also: End of the Age podcast December 31, 2018. "Who is the Antichrist?" https://www.endtime.com/end-of-the-age/who-is-the-antichrist-2/

9. Will the people in the United States have to take the Mark of the Beast?
End of the Age podcast February 8, 2019, 39:55 minutes into the show through marker 41. "Open Line 327." https://www.endtime.com/end-of-the-age/open-line-327/

10 Who is the false prophet?
Understanding the ENDTIME Lesson 8 DVD, The Antichrist and the False Prophet.

11. Where is Islam in the Bible?
Understanding the ENDTIME Lesson 3 DVD, Islam in Bible Prophecy - The Four Horsemen.

12. What are the seven trumpets? Have some of them already blown?

Yes, the first five trumpets have already blown.

Understanding the ENDTIME Lesson 12 DVD, The 7 Trumpets.

13. What are the seven seals? Have any of them been opened yet?

Yes, the first four seals have already been opened.

Understanding the ENDTIME Lesson 3 DVD, Islam in Bible Prophecy - The Four Horsemen.

14. Who are the 144,000 mentioned in Revelation 14 and when will they be "sealed"?

End of the Age podcast August 3, 2018, 50:25 minutes into the show through marker 52:57. "Open Line 303." https://www. endtime.com/end-of-the-age/open-line-303/

15. What is happening during the thirty minutes of silence described in Revelation 8:1? Is this the rapture taking place?

End of the Age podcast August 1, 2018, 48:30 minutes into the show through marker 50:35. "Secret Peace Talks." https:// www.endtime.com/end-of-the-age/secret-peace-talks/

Also: End of the Age podcast February 8, 2019, 45:07 minutes into the show through 46:51. "Open Line 327." https://www. endtime.com/end-of-the-age/open-line-327/

16. Will the wrath of God be worldwide or localized?

End of the Age podcast August 1, 2018, 50:35 minutes into the show through marker 52:35. "Secret Peace Talks." https://www.endtime.com/end-of-the-age/secret-peace-talks/

17. Is "he who now letteth will let" (KJV) referring to the Holy Spirit? (2 Thessalonians 2:6-7).

Archived End of the Age podcast January 2, 2019, 38 minutes into the show through marker 41:35. "The Coming End Time Revival 1."

https://www.endtime.com/end-of-the-age/end-time-revival/

Also: End of the Age podcast March 20, 2019, 50 minutes into the show through marker 54:05. "Trump-Netanyahu Meeting."

Also: End of the Age podcast October 14, 2019, 45 minutes into the show through marker 48:15. "Is the stage being set for the Battle of Armageddon?"
https://www.endtime.com/end-of-the-age/
is-the-stage-being-set-for-the-battle-of-armageddon/

18. Who are the "elect"?

End of the Age podcast August 8, 2019, 56 minutes into the show through marker 57:22. "Gil Hoffman Interview."
https://www.endtime.com/end-of-the-age/
gil-hoffman-interview/

19. Where will the Battle of Armageddon take place?

End of the Age podcast August 28, 2019, 45:40 minutes into the show through marker 47:00. "Arab Minister Willing to Join Moderate Left-Wing Government in Israel."

https://www.endtime.com/end-of-the-age/arab-minister-willing-to-join-moderate-left-wing-government-in-israel/

20. Will Christians be exempt from God's wrath?

End of the Age podcast August 3, 2018, 56:52 minutes into the show through marker 57:52. "Open Line 303."

https://www.endtime.com/end-of-the-age/open-line-303/

21. Is the "New Jerusalem" a symbolic representation of the Church?

End of the Age podcast August 3, 2018, 40:30 minutes into the show through marker 41:47. "Open Line 303."

https://www.endtime.com/end-of-the-age/open-line-303/

Endnotes

Chapter 1: The Time Machine

1. Genesis 6:15
2. Genesis 7:1-16

Chapter 3: Six Days

1. Genesis 1:2
2. Genesis 1:3
3. Genesis 1:16-19
4. Genesis 1:6-8
5. Genesis 1:9-10
6. Genesis 1:11-13
7. Genesis 1:16-19
8. Genesis 1:20-22
9. Genesis 1:24-31
10. Genesis 1:24-31

Chapter 6: That Day Will Not Come, Unless . . .

1. Acts 9:1-18 ESV
2. 2 Thessalonians 2:1-2 NIV
3. 2 Thessalonians 2:1-4 ESV (context includes verse 1)

Chapter 7: The Dead in Christ Will Rise First

1. Romans 8:1-11 ESV; Galatians 5:16-25 ESV

Chapter 8: The Last Trumpet

1. YouVersion.com. December 7, 2017 "YouVersion Bible App to Reach 300 Million Downloads by End of 2017. https://www.youversion.com/press/youversion-bible-app-reach-300-million-downloads-end-2017/

2. Biblica.com. "How many different languages has the Bible been translated into?" https://www.biblica.com/resources/bible-faqs/how-many-different-languages-has-the-bible-been-translated-into/

3. Bible.com. "How and when was the Bible divided into chapters and verses?" https://bible.org/question/how-and-when-was-bible-divided-chapters-and-verses

4. Acts 1:3 KJV

5. John 20:19-24 KJV

6. John 20:26-29 KJV

7. John 21:1-14 KJV

8. 1 Corinthians 15:6 KJV

9. Acts 1:4, 8-9 KJV

10. Acts 1:9-11 ESV

11. Rick Renner, A Light in Darkness, Seven Messages to the Seven Churches; Vol. One. 2010. p. 3. ISBN: 978-0-9779459-8-6

12. Revelation 1:19 KJV

Chapter 9: The Two Witnesses

1. Revelation 11:15 KJV
2. 1 Corinthians 15:51-53
3. 1 Thessalonians 4:16-17
4. 1 Thessalonians 4:15-17 KJV

Chapter 10: No One Knows the Day or the Hour

1. Mark 13:32; Matthew 24:36 NIV
2. Revelation 11:5 NIV
3. Revelation 11:6 NIV/AMP
4. Mark 13:23-33 NIV

Chapter 11: What Event Will Start the Final Seven Years?

1. Story told in Daniel 6
2. Story told in Daniel 3
3. Story told in Daniel 2
4. Daniel 12:4; 8-10 KJV
5. Daniel 9:27 NIV
6. Genesis 15:18 KJV
7. *EndTime* magazine. Nov/Dec 2020 issue; page 6. The two Arab countries that recognize Israel's right to exist are Egypt (1979) and Jordan (1994). In 2020, four additional Arab countries formally acknowledged Israel's right to exist: United Arab Emirates, Bahrain, Sudan, and the Kingdom of Morocco. They signed an agreement called the "Abraham Accords." None of these agreements, however, met all of the necessary prophetic requirements to

qualify as *the* agreement that will begin the final seven years. The primary requirement, of course, is that the Palestinians must be included in the agreement.

8. Genesis 12:4-7 ESV

Chapter 12: The Confirmation of the Covenant

1. 2 Thessalonians 2:1-4 ESV

Chapter 13: The Middle East Peace Agreement

1. *End of the Age* podcast. February 5, 2020, 9:00 into the show through marker 12:01. "Will Trump's "Deal of the Century" Succeed?" https://www.endtime.com/end-of-the-age/will-trumps-deal-of-the-century-succeed/

2. *End of the Age* podcast. January 13, 2020, 31 minutes into the show through marker 32:10, "Trumps Peace Agreement Released Within the Next Two Weeks?" https://www.endtime.com/end-of-the-age/trumps-peace-agreement-released-within-the-next-two-weeks/

3. *End of the Age* podcast. March 4, 2019, 11:30 into the show through marker 12:15. "Peace Plan Update." https://www.endtime.com/end-of-the-age/peace-plan-update-3/

4. *End of the Age* podcast. August 28, 2019, 48:38 into the show through marker 50:12. "Arab Minister Willing to Join Moderate Left-Wing Government in Israel." https://www.endtime.com/end-of-the-age/arab-minister-willing-to-join-moderate-left-wing-government-in-israel/

5. *End of the Age* podcast. March 4, 2019, 12:15 into the show

through marker 12:25. "Peace Plan Update." https://www.
endtime.com/end-of-the-age/peace-plan-update-3/

6. *End of the Age* podcast. August 28, 2019, 48:38 into the
show through marker 50:12. "Arab Minister Willing to
Join Moderate Left-Wing Government in Israel." https://
www.endtime.com/end-of-the-age/arab-minister-will-
ing-to-join-moderate-left-wing-government-in-israel/

7. *End of the Age* podcast. March 4, 2019, 12:25 into the show
through marker 12:55. "Peace Plan Update." https://www.
endtime.com/end-of-the-age/peace-plan-update-3/

8. *End of the Age* podcast. August 28, 2019, 48:38 into the
show through marker 50:12. "Arab Minister Willing to
Join Moderate Left-Wing Government in Israel." https://
www.endtime.com/end-of-the-age/arab-minister-will-
ing-to-join-moderate-left-wing-government-in-israel/

9. *End of the Age* podcast. August 7, 2019, 39:41 into the
show through marker 41:08. "Behind the Scenes of the
Peace Plan." https://www.endtime.com/end-of-the-age/
behind-the-scenes-of-the-peace-plan/

10. *End of the Age* podcast. August 28, 2019, 48:38 into the
show through marker 50:12. "Arab Minister Willing to
Join Moderate Left-Wing Government in Israel." https://
www.endtime.com/end-of-the-age/arab-minister-will-
ing-to-join-moderate-left-wing-government-in-israel/

11. *End of the Age* podcast. March 4, 2019, 12:57 into the show
through marker 13:22. "Peace Plan Update." https://www.
endtime.com/end-of-the-age/peace-plan-update-3/

12. *End of the Age* podcast. August 7, 2019, 38:31 into the show through marker 39:38. "Behind the Scenes of the Peace Plan." https://www.endtime.com/end-of-the-age/behind-the-scenes-of-the-peace-plan/

13. *End of the Age* podcast. September 2, 2019, 44:10 into the show through marker 45:17. "Israeli Elections & The Peace Plan." https://www.endtime.com/end-of-the-age/israeli-elections-the-peace-plan-2/

14. *End of the Age* podcast. January 13, 2022, 8:20 into the show through marker 10:15. Also, 17:30 into the show through marker 19:38. "Middle East Peace in 2022?" https://www.endtime.com/end-of-the-age/middle-east-peace-in-2022/

Chapter 17: Will Christians Be on the Earth During the Final Three-and-a-Half Years?
1. Revelation 20:4 KJV

Chapter 18: Bringing the Saints with Him
1. Zechariah 14:1-5 KJV, specifically verse 5
2. John 3:1-8 KJV

Chapter 19: The Lord Will Come Like a Thief in the Night
1. 1 Thessalonians 5:2-5 ESV
2. Revelation 9:7-10 ESV

Chapter 20: The Island
1. Acts 27:37

2. 2 Corinthians 11:25-27

3. Acts 28:31

Chapter 21: The Wrath of Satan

1. *End of the Age* podcast. February 22, 2019, 37:13 minutes into the show through marker 40:16. "Open Line 329." https://www.endtime.com/end-of-the-age/open-line-329/

2. Revelation 12:12, 17 ESV

Chapter 22: The Wrath of God

1. Revelation 16:1KJV; Romans 1:18

2. Revelation 16:2 ESV

3. Revelation 16:3 NIV

4. Revelation 16:4 NIV

5. Revelation 16:8-9 NIV

6. Revelation 16:10-11 NIV

7. Revelation 16:12, 16 NIV

8. Revelation 16:17-21 ESV

9. *End of the Age* podcast. October 30, 2019, 54:50 minutes into the show through marker 56:39. "Will You Make the Rapture?" https://www.endtime.com/end-of-the-age/will-you-make-the-rapture-3/

Chapter 23: The Time of the End

1. Daniel 12:4 ESV

Chapter 24: A Time for Decision

1. Revelation 13:7 KJV
2. Revelation 13:15-18 KJV; Revelation 14:9-11 KJV
3. 2 Timothy 3:1 KJV
4. 2 Timothy 3:12 ESV
5. According to Daniel 11:40, the Antichrist will have enemies. According to Daniel 11:41, the Antichrist will not gain control of Edom, Moab, and Ammon, which are all in the country of Jordan. "He shall enter also into the glorious land, and many countries shall be overthrown: but these shall escape out of his hand, even Edom, and Moab, and the chief of the children of Ammon" (Daniel 11:41 KJV). Israel and the United States of America will also not be under the control of the Antichrist. *End of the Age* podcast. February 8, 2019, 39:36 minutes into the show through marker 41:05. "Open Line 327." https://www.endtime.com/end-of-the-age/open-line-327/
6. *End of the Age* podcast. August 28, 2019, 53:20 into the show through marker 56:01. "Arab Minister Willing to Join Moderate Left-Wing Government in Israel." https://www.endtime.com/end-of-the-age/arab-minister-willing-to-join-moderate-left-wing-government-in-israel/ The nations which will become the center of the coming New World Order will be Germany, Russia, the UK, and a ten-nation alliance out of Europe, according to EndTime partner letter, April 2020, p. 2
7. John 16:7-9 ESV; Romans 3:10-12 KJV

8. Acts 2:38 KJV; Luke 13:3,5 ESV

9. John 14:16-17 KJV; Acts 2:38 KJV; 1 Corinthians 6:19 NIV

10. John 1:12-13 NIV; Galatians 3:24-26 KJV

11. Galatians 5:22-23 KJV; Romans 6:1-4 KJV; Ephesians 2:8-9 KJV

12. Colossians 1:13-14 AMP; John 15:11 AMP; 1 Corinthians 15:1-5 AMP; Ephesians 5:2 AMP

13. John 15:1-17 AMP; Ephesians 5:1-2 AMP; Galatians 5:22-23 AMP

14. 1 Corinthians 6:19-20 NIV

15. Galatians 2:20, 5:24 AMP; Mark 8:35 AMP; Luke 9:23 AMP

16. Revelation 21:8 KJV

17. Deuteronomy 5:11 New American Standard, The Lockman Foundation 1977

18. Matthew 5:28 ESV

19. Conversation adapted from *The Way of the Master Study Guide* by Kirk Cameron and Ray Comfort; pp. 99-106; Genesis Publishing Group, 2006. Used with permission. LivingWaters.com.

20. 2 Corinthians 5:17-21 AMP

21. Ephesians 2:8-10 AMP

Acknowledgments

Thank you, God, for planting the seed in me to write what I have learned and for orchestrating all the pieces of the puzzle to completion. This book could not have been accomplished without all the people you divinely lined up in advance to help me.

I am ever so grateful to my team of incredible editors, who are so perceptive, knowledgeable, and each played an integral part in the completion of this book. I'm especially thankful for Lyle Jensen and Bill Poehler, who made themselves available throughout the editing process. The countless hours you both gave of your time and skills will never be forgotten. Thank you also to Keilah Frickson, Kenn Fukuda, Dave Garner, Mackenzie Grubbs, and Anna Witherington for your insight, suggestions, and corrections that all worked together to improve End Time Machine.

Thank you to each of my special consultants who provided valuable input in their respective areas of expertise: Captain Titus "Axel" Amundson, Samuel Hatman, Jeremy Jacobs, Aharon Levarko, and Julie Te Slaa.

Thank you to all of my proofreaders who contributed feedback and critical commentary: Dawn Dahlberg, Sharon Barnes, Tom LaLonde, Thaddeus Latsa, Bonnie Menigo, Lee Nelson, Brian Nemanic, Kay Nemanic, Nancy Roach, Kyle Sirovy, Reagan Sirovy, and Laura Smith.

Thank you to all my pre-tribulation friends who unknowingly inspired me to write. The development of my story was largely a result of our many end-time conversations. I'm grateful for your continued friendships even though we disagree regarding the sequence of end-time events.

Thank you, Reed, my best friend and husband of thirty-two years. You played a significant role with your computer skills, valuable input, research assistance, continual encouragement, and belief in me.

I am so grateful to the late Irvin Baxter for obeying God's plan for his life and for giving his blessing to my inclusion of him in this fictional story. His excellent teaching on a complicated and controversial subject continues to help many people. This book would not have been possible without his faithful teaching ministry. He is greatly missed.

Thank you, Ray Comfort and Kirk Cameron, for your faithfulness in evangelism. Your witnessing experiences on YouTube are great examples for all of us.

About the Author

K elli Nelson began listening online to Irvin Baxter in 2008 and soon became passionate about his end time teaching. In an attempt to convince her friends that the rapture of the church will happen after the tribulation, Kelli developed a flip chart and used it to explain why, in her view, the Scriptures support a post tribulation rapture. After receiving requests for copies of her chart—which supported her oral presentation but was not meant to be read as a book—she challenged herself to creatively present her arguments in written form. The result is *End Time Machine*. Kelli is pictured in the saddle on the Mount of Olives, part of her 2015 tour of Israel with EndTime Ministries.

Made in the USA
Monee, IL
18 July 2024